Advances in Mining Science and Technology, 7

Electromagnetic Compatibility in Underground Mining Selected Problems

Advances in Mining Science and Technology

Advisory Editor: B. N. Whittaker
                Mining Engineering Department, University of Nottingham
                Nottingham, Great Britain

Advances in Mining Science and Technology, 7

ELECTROMAGNETIC COMPATIBILITY IN UNDERGROUND MINING
Selected Problems

**Florian Krasucki, Kazimierz Miśkiewicz,
Antoni Wojaczek, Stanisław Frączek**

Institute of Electrical Engineering and Automation of Mining
Silesian Technical University, Gliwice, Poland

Edited by: **Florian Krasucki**

ELSEVIER
Amsterdam—London—New York—Tokyo

PWN—POLISH SCIENTIFIC PUBLISHERS
Warszawa

1993

Translated by *Adam Nieoczym*. Revised and updated translation of the Polish edition *Wybrane zagadnienia kompatybilności elektromagnetycznej w górnictwie*, published in 1988 by Państwowe Wydawnictwo Naukowe, Warszawa

Exclusive sales rights
in Albania, Bulgaria, Commonwealth of Independent States, Croatia, Cuba, Czecho-Slovakia, Estonia, Hungary, Korean People's Democratic Republic, Latvia, Lithuania, Mongolia, People's Republic of China, Poland, Romania, Slovenia, Vietnam and Yugoslavia
POLISH SCIENTIFIC PUBLISHERS PWN LTD.
Miodowa 10, 00-251 Warszawa, Poland

in all remaining areas
ELSEVIER SCIENCE PUBLISHERS B.V.
Sara Burgerhartstraat 25
P.O. Box 211, 1000 AE Amsterdam, The Netherlands

Library of Congress Cataloging-in-Publication Data

Wybrane zagadnienia kompatybilności elektromagnetycznej w górnictwie.
  English
  Electromagnetic compatibility in underground mining: selected problems/Florian Krasucki ... [et al.; translated by Adam Nieoczym].
    p. cm. — (Advances in mining science and technology; 7)
  Translation of: Wybrane zagadnienia kompatybilności elektromagnetycznej w górnictwie.
  Includes bibliographical references and index.
  ISBN 0-444-98670-7
    1. Electricity in mining. 2. Electromagnetic compatibility. I. Krasucki, Florian. II. Nieoczym, Adam. III. Title. IV. Series.
  TN343.W9313 1992
    622—dc20   92-12277
                                                                                          CIP

ISBN 0-444-98670-7

Printed in Poland by D.N.T.

Preface

Electromagnetic interactions have always been present in nature and the problem of protection against them or of reducing their effects is at least as old as the practial application of electric energy both for power purposes and as an information carrier. Electromagnetic compatibility, understood as the ability of a system to oppose the influence of the electromagnetic environment with no unacceptable limitations of its operational possibilities, is currently becoming of particular importance, as a result of the rapid development of electronic systems and devices (and in particular microelectronics) and their widespread application throughout industry, including mining and particularly in systems vital to the operation and safety of mines.

The present work considers selected problems of electromagnetic interactions in mining. The selection was done on the basis of a topical analysis of present day mining environments and current developments in mine electrification and automatization, and in particular the development of computer control systems. Basic definitions are given together with information regarding potential sources of interaction, and their effects, in a mine environment, with special regard for the specific character of the underground mining environment.

The problem of electromagnetic interference has been analysed according to the scheme: causes (sources) of the disturbances—condition of their propagation (transmission)—effects (receivers) of interference.

The principal part of the present work is devoted to a discussion of the electromagnetic interactions, which occur and are transferred in power networks and in electric traction systems. These are the most important sources of disturbances both as regards their level (power) and their virtually unlimited potential to transfer "local" interferences even to distant receivers. This is mostly the result of the fact that under mine conditions, the close location and sometimes common installation of power and telecommunication lines are unavoidable. The possible effects of interactions and the corresponding protective means and measures are discussed on the basis of examples relating to the control systems, safety control systems and systems of telephone communication used at present in Polish underground mines. The present work illustrates the indispensability of proper, passive and active, environmental co-ordination, namely such co-ordination which takes into account the mutual uniformity of the structure and operating conditions of all the electric devices used in mining, i.e., total electromagnetic compatibility (EMC).

In the present study, the results of research carried out at the Institute of Electrical Engineering and Automation of Mining, Silesian Technical University in Gliwice, in co-operation with the Research and Production Centre for Mining Electrotechnics and Automatics EMAG in Katowice have been primarily used. The analyses and measurements were carried out under actual working conditions in underground coal mines, but the discussion and conclusions are of a more general nature and may be used in other plants with similar environmental conditions and electric systems.

Co-authors of particular sections are: Kazimierz Miśkiewicz — Sections 2.6, 3.6, 4.5–4.12, 5.11, 5.12; Antoni Wojaczek — Sections 3.7, 4.2–4.4, 5.2–5.10; Stanisław Frączek — Sections 5.13.2, 5.13.3.

Florian Krasucki

Contents

1 Introduction

The present state of the production of minerals and the further development of mining depends on an up-to-date range and level—and on the indispensable further development—of electrification and automatization of mines.

Due to the substantial coal resources in Poland and the lack of other substitute fuels, coal shall remain the basic source of energy in this country for many years. Further development of the Polish coal mining industry and coal production is being planned, which is further influenced by the intended processing of hard coal into products. It is planned to obtain this increase in hard coal production from both new mines in the Rybnik and Lublin Coal Districts as well as through the modernization and further development of existing mines (primarily by working deeper strata). It is also important to take into account that both in the new mines being planned and in the existing ones, the deposit and mining conditions are systematically getting worse.

To obtain an economically viable production, it is necessary to apply technical and technological solutions, which take into account the changing natural conditions of the exploited deposits and which make it possible to keep in production costs as low as possible while at the same time ensuring a necessary level of safety. Meeting these requirements at the present stage of technological development also depends on the extent and nature of electrification and automatization methods in mining.

The method and extent of electrification and automatization exerts a direct influence on the technology of production in mines, the type of machines used, their output and power consumption. The techno-economic necessity for electrification is particularly well seen in the case of time-space concentration of production: while using very powerful machines with large outputs.

However, the use of an electric current causes an increase in hazards both for the mine itself and its personnel. First of all, there are dangers of electric shocks, an increase of stray currents, while the probability of mine fires and explosions also increases to a great extent.

The hazards associated with electrification depend on many factors, such as: type of mining compartments (presence of explosive mixtures, humidity, temperature), geological conditions (rock firmness, tendency for crumps and break-downs), exploitation systems, systems of mechanization and types of mining machines as well as the human (anthropogenic) factor. The possibility of the appearance of an individual type of hazard depends each time on the simultaneous existence of both a potential cause and favourable environmental conditions, which mostly depend on the technological environmental conditions (mine compartments and headings). Therefore, the necessity to meet the requirements concerning the methods and means for eliminating, or at least reducing, the mine hazards shall be considered first as being of prime importance. For example, in methane-rich mines, this relates first of all to the ventillation of electrified mine workings and to monitoring the mine atmosphere.

The second group of important requirements is met by ensuring a high quality of technological equipment supplied, which should be suited to the environmental conditions prevailing in a mine. It is also necessary to ensure appropriate maintenance and preservation of the equipment used. These requirements also apply to the means of electrification and automatization, which must be designed, manufactured and operated, so that a safe, reliable and effective operation can be ensured under the expected technological conditions of the environment of mining plants.

Safety is one of the principal criteria for assessing the possibilities and effects of human activity in a mining plant. The required level of safety may be achieved using appropriate protection (prophylactic means) against the occurrence of hazards together with protection against their effects [18].

The entire problem should be discussed on a broad basis, however, improvement should also be sought for in partial solutions, which should concern individual elements of the system, which, in the general meaning of this word, comprises a mine.

Modern mines can be characterized by a great concentration of various technological devices, including electric equipment, used directly in the process of production (particularly at the working face) as well as in other complementary processes and units of mine structure. The obvious interdependence between safety and the reliability of equipment is best seen in the case of the electrification and automatization systems of mines. Unreliability of equipment, which may cause hazards may be the source or effect of various disturbances. In the case of electric equipment the interferences of an electromagnetic nature are of great qualitative and quantitative importance (i.e. have a great range and effect). Their negative effects are first of all manifested by the improper operation of the so-called weak-current systems (systems of control, monitoring, warning, telephone communication), which often co-decide about production and the state of mine safety.

2 General Principles, Concepts and Terms

2.1 The technological environment—environmental protection

Technological devices can be operated under various environmental conditions. The location and the mode of operation comprise the most general factors, which influence the conditions under which the device operates. It is obvious that a device installed outside or inside a building, in water, in the ground, or underground in a mine, shall be in different operational conditions. For general-purpose devices it is usually assumed that atmospheric conditions like temperature, pressure, air humidity, precipitation, air contamination, smokiness and the presence of caustic and explosive gases are of decisive importance.

Under the concept of *environment*, we understand the area, in which there are present certain combinations of natural physico-chemical and biotic factors (mostly climatic—the natural environment), as well as various factors resulting from human activity and human presence, other living creatures and technological devices [52]. The *technological environment* is an area (environment) where both natural environmental elements as well as factors representing the effects of the presence and/or operation of technological devices are present. The part of an area close to a device, filled with air or any other medium is called its *surroundings*.

The environmental factors may influence a device (a system) in a certain way (positively or negatively), which depends on the degree of sensitivity of individual elements, devices or the entire system. Similarly, devices may influence the environment (including e.g. other devices). Factors acting from the direction of the environment onto a device are called *stressing factors*, while those acting from a device onto the environment are termed *hazard factors*.

In mines, practically almost all the types of factors under highly hazardous environmental conditions occur, as a result of which the hazard for the equipment is very high. However, the most important factors are those resulting, directly or indirectly, from the technological activity of man [18].

The specificity of the technological environment in underground mine workings results first of all from the high intensity and the cumulation of stresses and from the fact that this environment is mostly created by technological and organizational factors. One shall assume that man is the principal factor, which shapes the technological environment of a mine and the means of environment protection. An underground mine working represents a *technological microclimate* and in many cases we deal with a *techno-cryptoclimate*.

As a potential source of environmental hazards for equipment installed in mines, and also taking into account that the environment is susceptible to dangers presented by this equipment, one should first of all consider the factors or their complexes, which characterize [18]: mine air (its composition and temperature, humidity, dustiness, content of explosive and caustic gases), and mine waters. In mining practice, other factors, characterizing the technological conditions of the environment, whose nature and intensity is, to a considerable extent, the effect of organization, technology and technique of production, geological structure and incidents, may be of much greater importance.

Generally, the technological environment of a mine may be characterized by detailing:

— climatic conditions (which include chemical and biotic phenomena) concerned with the properties of the atmosphere of the place, in which the equipment is being installed, stored or transported,
— organizational and technological conditions, resulting from the type of organization and the production process as well as systems of electric power networks and equipment design.

Of the wide variety of climatic phenomena present in underground mines, the following stress factors, which here are substantially more intense than at the surface [18], should be selected: air temperature, humidity, precipitation, chemical composition of the atmosphere and mine water, content of explosive gases in the atmosphere, dustiness, influence of mould and other microorganisms.

Of the techno-organizational fators, specific to mining, the following

are given: inclination, thickness and depth of coal seam, rock movements, rock and gas bursts, explosiveness of gases and dust, flammability
of materials, the method and degree of ventillation, demethanization, the
method of extraction and the depth of mining work, lack of sunlight and
natural ventilation, degree of mechanization, type and quality of mining
machines and their mode of operation, quality of structures, materials
and design of electric equipment, systems of power network and
telecommunication, type and range of their protective devices and mode
of operation, incidents (including e.g. short-circuits, overvoltages, stray
currents) and the means (system) of limiting, preventing and reducing
their effects. In prophylactics, it is important not only to be aware of the
potential occurrence of certain conditions and hazards, but also what
constitutes an environmental protection.

Creating an *environmental protection* consists of the use of appropriate
design solutions, materials, technological processes and organizational
actions, which aim at the correct operation of equipment, according to
the requirements. Thus, it includes those actions aimed at giving the
equipment features of environmental resistance (to certain stressing
factors) as well as environmental safety, which protects the environment
against certain hazards.

Environmentally-conscious manufacture of equipment should ensure
a minimal detrimental environmental effect, i.e. the ability to operate as
required with a certain reliability, over a certain life period together with
the ability to reduce associated hazards to acceptable levels under the
given environmental conditions. Thus, in mining, environmental coordination, i.e. appropriate adjustment of equipment to the expected
stressing factors (active coordination) and the creation of a suitable
environment (passive coordination), is indispensable. In mines, passive
coordination is extremely important, i.e. appropriate creation of the
environmental conditions, e.g. appropriate ventilation in methane-rich
mines and the appropriate choice and operation of equipment in order
to minimize hazards.

The electromagnetic field is one of the environmental factors.
Wherever an alternating electric current flows, there occurs a frequency
band, which may disturb other devices (systems). The electromagnetic
field also includes those charges and currents, which do not alter with
time and which produce static electric or magnetic fields. Environmentally-conscious manufacture of many devices should thus consider the

fact that they may operate in such an environment. This concerns in particular modern electronic equipment which is becoming more and more common, particularly in information systems. Their considerable band width and low signal levels cause an increase in sensitivity to disturbances, which is a few orders of magnitude higher compared the lamp systems used earlier. In practice, even good screening and/or the use of filters do not ensure full protection against disturbances.

With the development of the electronic systems, attempts are being made to reduce their susceptibility to disturbances. One of the directions of research is to investigate the phenomena (including the development of new research methods), which would make it possible to compare and practically evaluate the abilities of certain objects (devices, systems) for counteracting the disturbances. At the same time, at all points where it is advisable (and particularly in those systems, on which human life or e.g. mine safety depend), other non-electric variants of solutions shall be considered, even if they seem "old-fashioned and unattractive".

In the most general case *electromagnetic disturbances* should be treated as a group of stressing factors (natural and technological), and as potential hazards at the same time. In this approach, the environmentally conscious manufacture of a device (system) should also ensure the reduction of its capability to generate disturbances (environmental safety) as well as its own satisfactory insensity to disturbances (environmental resistance). Hence, from the point of view of electromagnetic interactions, the term *electromagnetic compatibility* is synonymous with the general concept of environmentally conscious manufacture of electric equipment. This type of manufacture (design) must also characterize the equipment (systems) manufactured to operate in a mining environment (mining equipment).

2.2 Hazards and interferences induced by the use of electric mining equipment

The occurrence of a state (situation, condition) which is dangerous to people, equipment or the environment is called a *hazard*. Hazards may result from natural causes or from human activity. They are often the result of mutual interactions of both groups of factors.

In mining plants various types of hazards similar to those of other industrial plants may occur. However, in mines, and in underground mines in particular, specific mine hazards occur, which are the effect of specific geological and mining conditions (e.g. fire, methane, water, or induced by crumps, rock and gas burst, coal-dust explosion).

In the environment of a mine, there are, besides the hazard resulting from natural causes, also the hazards related to human activity, including the hazard caused by the technological methods used. This group comprises the majority of the electric hazards induced by electric phenomena [18]. Their source may in some cases also be natural (e.g. telluric currents in the ground, atmospheric discharges, static electricity), however, the electric (power-electric, power-electronic, electronic and telecommunication) equipment is the most important source.

Static electricity (electrostatic phenomena) may serve as an example of electromagnetic dangers, not directly connected with electric equipment. Electrostatic charges may be formed during touch or friction of two solids, during motion of liquid, vapour or gases in pipelines and channels, during grinding and pouring of loose materials, during dust swirling in the air, during liquid filtration, by walking on insulating soles or over an insulating floor, while driving vehicles on tyres, etc. The charges cumulate and result in substantial energy increase ($W_c = 0.5\,CU^2$) and the increase of potentials in relation to the surrounding objects. In practice, the potentials of the charged objects may reach great values (e.g. swirling of coal dust—5.4 kV [18]).

Considerable increases in voltage cause the electric field intensity to exceed the electric strength of the surrounding air, and a spark discharge of the cumulated electrostatic energy takes place. Explosions and electric shock hazard may result from the uncontrolled firing of explosive materials (in blasting) while improper operation of electronic components in control and monitoring circuits may also take place.

The greatest danger in mines is the possibility of ignition of the mixture of flammable gases with air, or of the coal dust swirling in the air. In the latter case, an additional factor, which further increases the danger is the fact that the coal dust itself is a medium carrying electric charges and in addition it may self-ignite. Cases of methane ignition have been reported when air contaminated with coal dust flowed through ventubes made of synthetic materials. Static electricity has been the cause of many ignitions, in oil wells as well. Ignition from spark discharges at high voltage takes place at a substantially reduced energy level as compared with other causes of ignition. Most of the energy ($0.5\,CU^2$) is converted into heat almost immediately (since the co-called protective, cooling action of the electrodes is much lower) heating a small quantity of gas along the spark path to a very high temperature (1000–2000 K). The minimum energy W_{min} [18], required for the retain ignition of a methane-air mixture lies within the limits of 0.28 mJ ($C = 500$ pF, $U = 107$ V, constant distance between the electrodes) and 5 mJ ($C = 10$ nF, $U = 1$ kV, electrodes approach in each other). For coal dust this value is 40 mJ and it is considerably lower for the dusts of explosive materials. The minimum ignition impulse for electric detonators (common type) usually lies between 2.4 and 9 mJ, whereas for the co-called *safe detonators*, i.e. protected against stray currents, it varies from 40 to 93 mJ.

In practice, protection against electrization is usually ineffective. And thus, hazards caused by electrostatic charges are decreased by reducing their undesirable effects, and in the first instance by preventing their build up and draining them as soon as possible. The methods used most often are: earthing objects, on which the charges may be formed, increasing the electric surface conductivity, e.g. by increasing air humidity ($> 70\%$) and by the appropriate preparation of surfaces (mechanical or chemical coating with antistatic materials).

From the point of view of electrostatic phenomena, we are interested in the volume and surface resistance of the materials, on which the charges may be formed and cumulate. The time for which a given body may remain charged depends an the value of the resistance at given system capacity. Materials with a self-resistance (volume resistance) of 10^4 to 10^5 Ω m are still good conductors of electrostatic charges. Surface resistance also depends to a great extent on the condition of the surface (dust, contamination) and air humidity; usually a value of $R_s < 10^8$ Ω is assumed to represent the limiting value of surface resistance in electrostatics.

Assuming the minimum energy (W_{min}) to have a value of 0.27–5 mJ, it has been calculated that the surface resistance R_s of the conveyor belts used in mines should not exceed 0.14×10^8 to 2.5×10^8 Ω. The largest value for the potential of conveyor belts made of antistatic synthetic materials, measured in Polish coal mines was 120 V.

The build-up of electric charges on the clothes of workers employed in a mine may also be very important. The spark discharges between the head and shell of electric detonators caused by the charges gathered by employees transporting the charges may be a substantial danger. In experimental research, firing of detonators was found to be caused by: electrified clothes, boots, absorbers, and cap lamps. Short-circuiting the detonator wires while distributing or transporting them reduces, but does not exclude the probability of uncontrolled firing of the detonator. For this reason, the clothes of the employees carrying the detonators should be made of natural fibres with a minimal content of synthetic fibres; it is recommended that the resistance of footwear does not exced 5×10^8 Ω and that of clothing 10^9 Ω.

In dry headings, where the relative humidity of the air does not exceed 70%, it is recommended to wet the shooting holes before charging them.

In the literature, attention is paid even to the possibility of causing ignition of methane-air mixtures through electrostatic charges gathered on the wires used for measuring the electrostatic potential in ventilation channels, as well as on the elements of shaft hoists.

Electric hazards may be indirect cause of other mining hazards, e.g. fire and explosion dangers. The specificity of mining conditions results in a high interdependence of the hazards taking place in mines whilst possibility of their occurrence and intensity varies with time. Of the electric devices used in mines, the most important sources of potential hazards are power networks (devices) used for the transformation and transmission of electric energy. In practice, these circuits can be found in every heading and compartment during every stage of development of an electrified mine.

Telecommunication devices and circuits in which the electric current acts as a carrier of information and orders, are used both over a limited range (space) in systems of control, warning and monitoring of the state of machine operation (local automatics) and in more extensive systems, primarily in dispatching. The most extensive of these is the system for monitoring mine safety, which includes the following subsystems: monitoring the physical parameters of mine atmosphere and ventilation control, methanometric protection and demethanization control, pre-detection of endogenic and exogenic fires, prediction of crumps, CO_2 breakouts and flows, and water drainage. Moreover, systems of crump danger control, production process control, crew movement control, supervision and management, as well as alarm systems and information are also used. In each mine, the telecommunication system consists of the system of communication throughout an entire mine (including the dispatch communication system), and local communications systems.

The conditions under which the electrical equipment operates substantially influence the possibility of electric hazards. Theses conditions can be divided into *systemic conditions*, which result from phenomena (mostly electric in nature) which occur in an electric system, and environmental conditions in the place where the equipment is operating.

Switching on the voltage and current flow in an electric circuit causes a voltage loading of insulation and a current loading of conducting elements. We can differentiate three types of operating conditions of electric equipment: working proper (e.g. idle, loading proper), working improper (transient, e.g. overload) and disturbance. In the most general case disturbance means a violation of the established order, improper functioning of something; it is that condition which represents a deviation from normal. A disturbance may be both effect and cause. For example a disturbance which occurs in any device may cause the improper operation of certain devices and proper operation of any devices may also induce disturbances in the operation of others.

In technological devices disturbances often are result of damage. It is a basic notion of the theory of reliability of technological objects that damage is manifested by the complete or partial loss, or change of the properties of an object, which cause that object (device, its subassemblies or elements) to be incapable of proper operation. Hence this notion has a broader meaning than that used in common speech. Damage is the effect of the action of a number of factors upon an object within a specific period of time. The factors may occur during operation of the device (both working and disturbed), during the period of storage or transport, or even during the process of manufacture. Damages may also be caused by design and production errors and by the improper use of such a device. In general terms it is a stochastic process, with a big contribution of anthropogenic factors. Most of the disturbances, which occur in mining are also of this character. Hence, it is difficult to determine a general, fixed set of properties to evaluate the ability of a device for proper, reliable (and thus safe) operation.

Electric mining devices, depending on their technological condition and operation, may be the cause of many different hazards, whose effect may be as follows:
— electric shock,
— electric ignition of flammable materials (electric fires),

— ignition of explosive mixtures (explosions of fire damp and coal dust),
— unintentional ignition of explosive materials (accidents in shooting),
— thermal burns and mechanical and acoustic traumas.

Usually, the causes of these hazards are: unshielded parts of equipment, electric circuits being under voltage exceeding the safe voltage or switched-off circuits being charged; stray voltages (damage, contact and pace voltages, earth voltages and currents); sparks or electric arcs and stray currents; parts of equipment heated to a temperature exceeding 70°C, and the moving parts of equipment.

The dangers caused by electromagnetic interaction (between electric equipment and people and between themselves, as well as interaction taking place within a single device) shall be treated separately. In practice, these interactions occur everywhere and continuously and their effects may only be noticed occasionally and be either harmful or not. Electromagnetic interaction upon a person may be manifested by biological changes; the most frequent symptoms are: a feeling of tiredness, headaches and disturbances in blood circulation. The cause of these are strong magnetic fields (high current values) and strong electric fields (very high voltages). Much more frequently electromagnetic interactions are the cause of disturbances in the operation of technological devices. In mining, these disturbances are first of all manifested by a deterioration in telephone communication and the improper operation of mining equipment control systems and dispatching systems. In general, it can be said that the type and condition of the electric equipment and the conditions and method of operating them (technological level and the range of electrification and automatization) determine the *state of electromagnetic compatibility in a mine*.

2.3   The electromagnetic field

Electromagnetic fields are the carriers of all the electromagnetic interactions. All the types of reaction taking place between electric charges, both motionless (electric forces) and those in motion (electric current, magnetic forces) are called *electromagnetic interactions*. Motionless charges and direct electric currents constitute the source of static fields (elelctrostatic, magnetostatic), whereas single charges and alternating currents cause the formation of alternating electromagnetic fields.

Electromagnetic interactions are common in nature and play a specific part in the process of scientific cognition of the world and everyday life. They are, among others, the source of knowledge of both the structure of atoms and elementary particles as well as of the structure of macroscopic bodies. The electromagnetic interaction of elementary particles is explained by quantum electrodynamics. The well-known Maxwell–Faraday theory (classical electrodynamics) is used to explain macroscopic phenomena.

The basic (vector) quantities, which characterize an electromagnetic field are the electric field intesity $\mathbf{K}$, the magnetic induction $\mathbf{B}$, the magnetic field intensity $\mathbf{H}$ and the electric induction $\mathbf{D}$. The existence of an electromagnetic field around particles (charges) means that for any particle with a mass m and charge q, moving at velocity $\mathbf{v}$, there acts a force $\mathbf{F}$ consisting of two components: the electric field component $q\mathbf{K}$ and the magnetic field component $q\mathbf{v} \times \mathbf{B}$. This is expressed by the Lorentz formula and Newton's equation in the form:

$$\mathbf{F} = q(\mathbf{K} + \mathbf{v} \times \mathbf{B}), \tag{2.1}$$

$$\frac{d}{dt} m\mathbf{v} = q\mathbf{K} + q\mathbf{v} \times \mathbf{B}. \tag{2.2}$$

The system of Maxwell's equation describing the electromagnetic field can be defined in the following way:

$$\operatorname{div} \mathbf{D} = \varrho,$$

$$\operatorname{div} \mathbf{B} = 0,$$

$$\operatorname{curl} \mathbf{K} = -\frac{\partial \mathbf{B}}{\partial t},$$

$$\operatorname{curl} \mathbf{H} = \frac{\partial \mathbf{D}}{\partial t} + \mathbf{J}.$$

In the homogeneous and isotropic medium (ε, μ, γ—constants) we can assume that $\mathbf{D} = \varepsilon\mathbf{K} = \varepsilon_0\varepsilon_r\mathbf{K}$, $\mathbf{B} = \mu\mathbf{H} = \mu_0\mu_r\mathbf{H}$, $\mathbf{J} = \gamma\mathbf{K}$, and transform the Maxwell's equations into the following form:

$$\varepsilon_0\varepsilon_r \operatorname{div} \mathbf{K} = \varrho, \tag{2.3}$$

$$\operatorname{curl}\mathbf{K} = -\mu_0\mu_r\frac{\partial\mathbf{H}}{\partial t}, \tag{2.4}$$

$$\operatorname{div}\mathbf{B} = 0, \tag{2.5}$$

$$\frac{1}{\mu_0\mu_r}\operatorname{curl}\mathbf{B} = \varepsilon_0\varepsilon_r\frac{\partial\mathbf{K}}{\partial t} + \gamma\mathbf{K}, \tag{2.6}$$

where

    ε_0, μ_0 — dielectric and magnetic permeability of vacuum,
    ε_r, μ_r — relative dielectric and magnetic permeability,
    γ — conductivity,
    ϱ — electric charge density,
    $\mathbf{J}$ — electric current density.

From the first equation it follows that the stream of an electric field running through the surface surrounding a charge is proportional to the value of this charge, and from equation (2.4), that a magnetic field, alternating with time, produces a vortex electric field (Faraday's induction law). The third equation states that there are no single magnetic charges in nature (the lines of a magnetic field are always closed, contrary to the lines of an electric field, which may close and terminate on electric charges).

The fourth Maxwell's equation says that magnetic field results from the changes of an electric field with time, and from electric currents. These equations also state that in areas, in which there are no material particles (electric charges and currents), electric and magnetic fields may exist in the form of electromagnetic waves which propagate at a finite velocity $c = 2.997... \times 10^8$ m·s^{-1}. The wave equations have the form:

$$-\frac{1}{c^2}\frac{\partial^2\mathbf{K}}{\partial t^2} + \Delta\mathbf{K} = 0, \tag{2.7}$$

$$-\frac{1}{c^2}\frac{\partial^2\mathbf{B}}{\partial t^2} + \Delta\mathbf{B} = 0, \tag{2.8}$$

where:

$$c = \sqrt{\varepsilon_0\mu_0}\,. \tag{2.9}$$

2.4   Electromagnetic interferences—electromagnetic compatibility

Unwanted electromagnetic phenomena (transient, noise, signal) which accompany a useful signal are called *electromagnetic disturbances*. These usually are electromagnetic noise, made up of impulses of a random character, though more seldom they are periodical [66]. Frequently they originate from sources different from the source of the useful signal. Therefore, these types of interference may be divided as follows according to source:
- cosmic (electromagnetic radiation from space),
- atmospheric (atmospheric discharges),
- man-made (operation of electric power devices: electric power lines, commutator motors, connectors, etc. in both operative and disturbance conditions),
- other, including the device itself (telecommunication devices, cross-talk, thermal agitation noise, etc.).

Electromagnetic interference may be of a regular or random nature, i.e. disturbances which consist of a great number of separate disturbances appearing at random in time with a random amplitude distribution. These may be divided into [66]:
- selective (sinusoidal) with a line spectrum,
- fluctuating (noise) with a continuous spectrum,
- impulse, in the form of single impulse and impulse sequence with regular or random parameters,
- quasi-impulse, which are made by the superposition continuous and impulse disturbances.

According to the PN-80/T-01005 standard it is assumed that a disturbance is long-lasting if the time of the duration is longer than 0.2 s (over 1 s it is called a hum). The short-lasting disturbances are classed as clicks if they have a duration time of up to 0.2 s and an interval of more than 0.2 s. Different devices (systems) may react differently to a given type of electromagnetic disturbance and may accordingly be called either *susceptible* or *resistant*. The notion of *electromagnetic compatibility*, in a general sense, means the ability of a device or an assembly of devices (system) to operate satisfactorily in a given electromagnetic environment while inducing no harmful disturbances into this environment (e.g. to other devices). In practice, there often occur for example radioelectric disturbances (i.e. disturbances which are electromagnetic in nature) which deform useful signals within the range of radio frequencies (15 kHz–100 GHz). These usually are industrial electromagnetic disturbances, generated in machines (e.g. sparking) or other devices produced by man as differentiated from natural disturbances.

In case of electronic devices, which are subject to radioelectric disturbance, it is assumed that the condition of electromagnetic compatibility reflects the ability of an electronic system (e.g. communication system) to operate in the presence of other electric systems, and they are neither influenced by, nor cause inadmissible deterioration of this operation as a result of unintentional sensitivity to these systems. At the same time, the electromagnetic disturbances which these systems themselves produce should not exceed permissible values. Appropriate maximum levels of disturbances and the minimum values of resistance to disturbances should be included in standards for all of apparatuses and devices.

The problem of electromagnetic compatibility forms part of the more general problem of environmental protection of products, i.e. the protection of products against certain stressing factors and the protection of the environment against hazards posed by the product. It is possible to obtain the condition of electromagnetic compatibility for various types of activities, by different methods. One of these methods involves determining the allowable levels of disturbances produced or received by electric devices. The results of the work done so far in the field of industrial radioelectic disturbances are reflected in the documents of CISPR, CCITT, IEC, and also in the publications of Polish Bureau of Standards issued under the common title Industrial Radioelectric Disturbances [53–71]. These standards specify permissible levels of disturbances [53, 55, 56, 57, 60, 61, 62, 65, 69], methods of investigating them and measuring devices [54, 67, 68, 70], as well as some of the means of prevention [58, 59, 63, 71]. To facilitate a uniform understanding and application of these standards, the notions used in the field of radioelectric disturbances are also defined in these publications. The group of general standards, concerned with telecommunication vocabulary (PNT-01001 through PNT-01012), may also be of help here.

The level of disturbances and means of protection are established by stating the values of voltage, current or disturbance power, or the strength of the interference field under standard conditions of measurement. At the same time, the permissible levels of industrial radioelectric disturbances, as laid down in individual standards for disturbing devices, are given in appropriate frequency intervals for the general range from 0.15 MHz to 300 (1000) MHz.

According to the principle adopted, the formulations of these standards are not specifically related to the equipment used in mining plants and it is necessary to take into consideration the specific nature of the natural and technological environment of an underground mine. For example, the specifications [82] concerning the interference of electric power lines and electric traction, worked out on the basis of CCITT materials [78] have been published in Polish as an appendix to the Regulation of the Ministers of: Communication, Power and Mining and Transport. However, they do not include underground systems. Thus, appropriate supplementary research is required into the variety of interactions in mine headings and their influence upon telecommunication lines.

2.5 The causes, nature and propagation of industrial electromagnetic interferences

In mining, and in particular in underground mines, electromagnetic disturbances are of vital importance.

The principal devices, which usually induce sinusoidal, noise, impulse and quasi-impulse electromagnetic interference [53], include:
— electric power lines and high-voltage devices,
— electric traction systems and locomotives,
— devices which supply power to other devices such as: thyristor converters, transformers, rectifiers for the charging of batteries stabilized feeders and transistor convertors,
— high frequency devices (industrial, medical, research) and radio and TV equipment.

Impulse and quasi-impulse disturbances produced by such devices as contact switching devices, rotating, commutator and ring-type electric machines, combustion engine spark-ignition devices and other equipment operating on the princple of electric discharge, may also be of great importance.

The relationship between electric devices, e.g. between electric power devices treated as a source of disturbances and a telecommunication chain can be presented in the form of a block diagram (Fig. 2.1). The primary signal $X(t)$ is transformed in the transmitter T into a form convenient for transmission through a telecommunication channel (e.g. through a wire, line, circuit) C to the receiver R. The interferences generated in the source propagate in various ways and influencing individual elements of the chain, may cause unwanted distortion of the received signal $X_0(t)$ relative to the transmitted signal $X(t)$. To determine the degree of distortion a knowledge of the sources of disturbances and the conditions of their propagation (couplings) and transmission in circuits is indispensable.

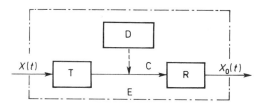

Fig. 2.1 Block diagram of a telecommunication chain: T—transmitter, R—receiver, C—channel, considering the disturbances (interferences) D in a coupling medium E

A telecommunication circuit is in general made up of a passive, four-terminal network, linear in principle, with arms elongated in the direction of the pairs of its terminals (longitudinal axis of the four-terminal network). In this context, the control circuits, for example, mining machinery made of complementary (auxiliary) conductors in flexible cables, may be treated as telecommunication circuits. The possible ways (couplings) in which disturbances may be propagated are presented schematically in Fig. 2.2 [7]. Conventionally, it is often assumed [29] that disturbances are propagated by conduction (at frequencies of less than 30 MHz) and by radiation (frequencies greater then 30 MHz). Physical quantities which characterize the sources of interferences (voltages, currents and intensities of field of interference may be described as either time functions or frequency functions. Due to the nature of the devices subject to disturbances, which are often characterized by band-pass frequencies, the description of disturbances in terms of frequency is the more useful. From this point of view we can differentiate the following: interferences with frequency of 50 Hz, disturbances with acoustic frequencies (including in mining some of less than twenty kHz) and radioelectric disturbances (above 15 kHz).

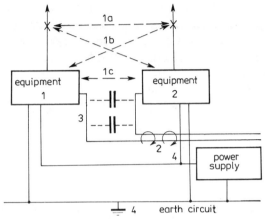

Fig. 2.2 Example of interference propagation paths: 1—radiation coupling between antennas (a), antennas and equipment housing (b), equipment housing with cabling (c); 2—inductive coupling between the cables; 3—capacitive coupling between the cables; 4—galvanic coupling in general circuits

In mining, the disturbances with frequencies of 50 Hz mostly have their source in electric power networks, in both working and interference conditions. They may produce voltages dangerous for servicing and insulation of the devices and interferences (voltages, currents) in auxiliary circuits in telecommunication networks. Preliminary investigations showed [31] that the principal causes of interferences within the range of acoustic frequencies in mines are the electric traction system dispatching loudspeaker systems, e.g. ALGUS (attending currents), intrinsical safe subscriber feeding bridges (IAUL) suppling the ATI-CB telephones (call-signal) and the circuits of warning and control systems incorporated in communication lines. Interferences with acoustic frequencies which occur in electric power networks and traction systems are carried along them and influence neighbouring circuits through couplings.

Radioelectric interferences influence first of all the long-wave radio-telephones used in electric (trolley) and storage-battery traction systems.

2.6   General principles of electromagnetic interference measurement

A selective voltmeter is the basic piece of equipment used for measuring interference voltages. To correctly interpret the measurements, it is indispensable to know the relation between the voltmeter reading and the spectrum and nature of the signal at its input. Such a voltmeter, called an *interference meter*, contains a superheterodyne circuit. A simplified block diagram of such a meter is presented in Fig. 2.3. This system contains four detectors, namely: peak detector, quasi-peak detector, average detector and r.m.s. detector. The peak detector is an envelope detector with a relatively low (as compared with the inverse of the medium frequency) charge time constant and a high discharge time constant. It permits impulse interference voltages with low frequency of repetition to be measured. The quasi-peak detector has three sets of values for the charge time constants t_c and discharge time constants t_d standardized for frequency ranges [29, 46]: (10–150) kHz: 45 ms and 500 ms, (0.15–30) MHz: 1 ms and 160 ms, (30–300) MHz: 1 ms and 550 ms.

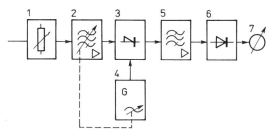

Fig. 2.3 Simplified structural diagram of interference meter: 1—voltage divider, 2—selective, tunable, high-frequency amplifier, 3—mixer, 4—generator (heterodyne), 5—intermediate frequency amplifier, 6—detector, 7—indicator

The average detector consists of a rectifier with a low-pass filter, which produces an averaging of the output voltage. When sinusoidal voltages are measured the readings of a voltmeter do not depend on the type of detector used and correspond to the r.m.s. value of input voltage. If a pulse train with spectrum density $F(j\omega)$ and repetition rate f_r is fed into a meter tuned into the frequency f_0, then its readings, depending on the type of detector used, will be equal to [46]:

$$\sqrt{2}\,F(j\omega_0)B_i \qquad \text{—for a peak detector,}$$
$$\sqrt{2}\,F(j\omega_0)P(\alpha)B_i \text{ —for a quasi-peak detector,}$$

$\sqrt{2}\,F(j\omega_0)f_r$ —for an average detector,

$\sqrt{2}\,F(j\omega_0)\sqrt{B_i}\,f_r$ —for a r.m.s. detector

respectively, where

$$\omega_0 = 2\pi f_0,$$

and B_i is the pulse bandwidth of the meter

$$B_i = \int\limits_0^\infty \frac{G(f)}{G(f_0)}\,df,$$

while $G(f)$ represents the frequency characteristics of the meter, i.e. the relation between the gain of the meter (the ratio of the voltage of the output of intermediate frequency amplifier to the voltage at the input of the meter) and the measured frequency f, $P(\alpha)$ is the function of the parameter $\alpha = \dfrac{t_c B_i}{t_d f_r}$ presented in Fig. 2.4.

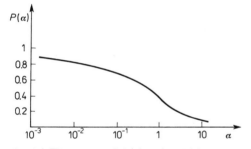

Fig. 2.4 The nature of the function $P(\alpha)$

If a noise with a spectral power density $S(\omega)$ is fed into the meter, then the readings will be equal to [29]:

$2.57\,\sqrt{S(\omega)B_s}$ —for a quasi-peak detector,

$1.25\,\sqrt{S(\omega)B_s}$ —for an average detector,

$\sqrt{2S(\omega)B_s}$ —for an r.m.s. detector,

where B_s is noise bandwidth of the meter, expressed by the formula

$$B_s = \int\limits_0^\infty \frac{G^2(f)}{G^2(f_0)}\,df. \tag{2.10}$$

Since the results of the measurements of pulse and noise interference depend on the bandwith of the meter, the spectral intensity is adopted as the measure of interference, i.e. the spectral density relative to bandwidth B_0 (e.g. 1 MHz) [29].

The spectral intensity U_w in the band B_0 is expressed by the relation

$$U_w[\mathrm{dB(\mu V/MHz)}] = U_p[\mathrm{dB(\mu V)}] + 20\log\frac{B_0}{B_i}, \qquad (2.11)$$

where U_p is the peak value of interference measured with a meter pulse bandwidth B_i.

Interference voltages are measured in the systems presented in Fig. 2.5. In the case of low-power devices an "artificial mains network" is used (Fig. 2.5a), which makes it possible, among others, to attenuate the interference occurring in the supply network and a rated loading of the device under test within the range of frequencies being measured. For devices with a rated voltage higher than 380 V or a rated current exceeding 25 A, the measurements are carried out in a system as presented in Fig. 2.5b, taking into account the attenuation introduced by the divider consisting of capacity C and input resistance of the meter (Fig. 2.5b).

(a)   (b)

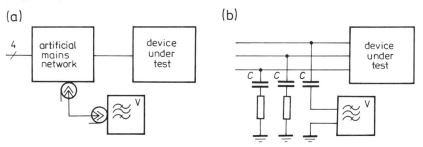

Fig. 2.5 The principle of measuring the interference voltage: (a) for "low power" equipment ($\leqslant 25$ A, $\leqslant 380$ V), (b) for "high power" equipment (> 25 A or > 380 V).

Interference voltages relative to earth should be measured in two ways: asymmetric (between the conductor and the earth) and symmetric (between the wires of the circuit). The interference current should be measured with a selective voltmeter using a current transformer or shunt. The measurements are often carried out after shorting the source of interference with a non-inductive condenser C_0 to obtain the so-called current efficiency of the source of interference (Fig. 2.6). Appropriate antennas are used for measuring the strength of the interference field. Within the frequency range of 0.01–30 MHz, a loop antenna tuned to the resonance frequency is used for measuring the magnetic component, whereas for measuring the electric component a stub antenna is used. Within the frequency range 30–300 MHz, the electric component only is measured with a tuned dipole antenna. The general conditions, in which the interference measurements should be carried out are laid down in the appropriate standards, e.g. [53, 67, 70].

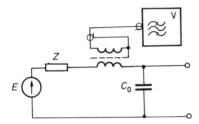

Fig. 2.6 System for measurement of interference current

The results of interference measurements (of voltages, currents, powers and electric field intensities) are given in either absolute values, using appropriate multiplies of the SI system (of voltage, current intensity or field strength) or alternatively, in relative values as a logarithm of the ratio of a measured value of a periodic signal (most often of amplitude strength or power) and the adopted reference value. The relative values are expressed in nepers (Np) if natural logarithms (ln) are used, and in decibels (dB) for common logarithms (log).

In practice, the following reference values are employed:

voltage — $U_0 = 0.775$ V or 1 µV,
current — $I_0 = 1.29$ mA or 1 µA,
power — $P_0 = 1$ mW (0.775 V, 600 Ω),
electric field intensity $K_0 = 1 \dfrac{\text{µV}}{\text{m}}$.

3 Electromagnetic Interactions Due to Alternating Current Power Networks

3.1 Types and range of interaction

The space surrounding a device (e.g. a line) is filled with the energy of an electric field and a magnetic field of strengths W_K and W_H, respectively, where

$$W_K = \frac{1}{2}\varepsilon_0\varepsilon_r\mathbf{K}^2,$$ (3.1)

and

$$W_H = \frac{1}{2}\mu_0\mathbf{H}^2,$$ (3.2)

where:

$\mathbf{K}, \mathbf{H}$ — electric and magnetic field intensity,
ε_0, μ_0 — electric and magnetic permeability of a vacuum,
ε_r — relative electric permeability of air.

The disturbing interaction of electric fields is mainly evident in the case of high voltage lines (high intensity of electric field $\mathbf{K}$), whereas the interaction of magnetic fields is also substantial in the case of low-voltage networks, particularly in cases involving the flow of currents of high intensity (e.g. short-circuit currents and starting currents). These fields may negatively influence man, animals and plants, and especially technological devices; they may cause biological disturbances and electric interferences.

As far as the influence on humans is concerned, the electric field intensity, particularly in the vincinity of high voltage overhead transmission lines (the magnetic component of the field with its relatively insignificant strength is neglected) is of prime importance. This happens for example in open cast mines. The value of the electric field intensity is the greatest in the centre of the span of an overhead cable and drops off towards the supports (where the height of suspension of the cables is the greatest and the supports also have a screening influence) and also with lateral distance away from the cables. In practice, the intensity of the electric field at height of two meters is the same as on the surface of the ground; the protection zone begins at the distance of 10 meters from the projection of the outer cables (at the distance greater than 40 meters from a line the influence of the electric field is pratically imperceptible). The interaction may be subjective, manifested by various sensations and feelings experienced by a person, and objective, i.e. the reception of field energy by a human acting as a capacitive receiving antenna. In the case of subjective interaction, we can assume that an electric field with intensity of 10–20 kV/m represents an electric threshold, which, after a certain period of time, may lead to unfavourable lesions in an organism. Thus, the values of electric field intensity, time and distance determine the possibility of a person remaining in the vicinity of the cable. Approximate permissible values are as follows: 15–20 kV/m over 1.5 hr during a working day in the protection zone and 1–2 kV/m for dwelling places.

In the case of objective interaction, an electric current flows through a person, and causes specific reactions in his body. Electric shocks may be experienced by a person when touching and discharging unearthed devices or structures being within the range of an electromagnetic field, or when touching earthed objects by a person insulated from the ground. The phenomenon of partial discharge (corona discharge) is also related to an electric field. It causes acoustic noises and interferences in radio and TV reception, communication and control system, in the operation of digital computers, protective devices, etc.

As far as the interaction of power lines with technological devices in general is concerned, we shall examine the occurrence of electric and magnetic fields (electromagnetic fields), which usually occur simultaneously, taking into account electric and magnetic couplings, and occasionally also galvanic couplings. The voltages of capacity charging and voltages induced in a switched-off circuit of a double-circuit line may serve as an example. Voltages induced in the conductors and metallic structures adjoining the line may cause certain disturbances (e.g. sparking) in other devices (e.g. radioelectric devices) and endanger safety (e.g. electrocution, fire, explosion). One should also consider the unwanted effects of inductive and galvanic interaction (electric current field at earthing points) of overhead power lines upon telecommunication lines and cable sheathing pipelines (tubes), even underground ones. Particularly important are cases of single-phase short-circuits in power lines with an earthed neutral point (e.g. 110 kV). Electrocuting with touch and step voltages and damage to cable insulation could be mentioned as the most obvious examples of hazard effects. From preliminary measurements it has been found that the potential of gas pipelines relative to earth reaches a value of up to 500 V, the electrocutive voltage may be 150 V and the voltage between gas pipelines and cable supports, in which a short-circuit took place, falls within the range of 1500–6700 V.

In deep mines, underground power networks (except electric traction lines) are constructed exclusively of cable lines. Insulated conductors, mostly armoured cables and flexible mining cables are used. In such networks, disturbances caused by electromagnetic interaction are most probable, and manifest themselves by the occurrence of parasitic voltages, induced in neighbouring conductors (or cores), which do not form point of the power circuits. In particular, this applies to the electric circuits made up by supplementary cores (protective, control, monitoring or measurement wires), which are bundled together with the operating cores inside cables and flexible cables. Voltages (electromotive force) may also be induced in the conductive sheaths and armouring of cables. The magnetic fields of electric power circuits may be the cause of other disturbances as well, particularly in adjoining telecommunication lines. Besides the electric lines enumerated above, the principal sources of radioelectric interference in mines are:

— traction systems and electric locomotives,
— static convertors, particularly of the thyristor type, and transformers,
— electric machines employing commutators,
— contact switches.

3.2 Theoretical principles of calculating the electromotive force of electromagnetic induction

Electric charges and currents flowing through a cable produce an inducted electric field, which may be treated as a generalized electric field. The electromotive force of induction is expressed by a general formula [39]:

$$e = \oint_l K \, dl = \oint_l (K_{ind} + K_{kin}) dl = -\frac{d\phi}{dt},$$ (3.3)

where

K_{ind} — inducted electric field in a motionless conductor related to the alternation (in time t) of a magnetic field,

K_{kin} — electromotive field (Laplace's field) induced in a moving conductor,

ϕ — magnetic flux.

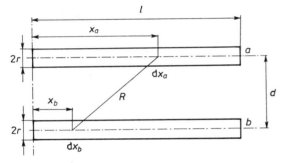

Fig. 3.1 Schematic diagram of two parallel conductors

Let us consider two linear circuits a and b at a distance d as in Fig. 3.1. If an alternating (AC) current (i_a) flows in circuit a then an inducted electromotive force is produced in circuit b according to the law of electromagnetic induction

$$e = -\frac{d\phi_{ab}}{dt},$$ (3.4)

where

ϕ_{ab} — flux originating in the a circuit and permeating into the b circuit.

According to Stokes' theorem, the flux ϕ_{ab} is equal to the circulation along b of a vector potential A_a induced by the current i_a, i.e. [39]:

$$\phi_{ab} = \int_b A_a dx_b = \int_a \int_b \frac{\mu}{4\pi} i_a \frac{dx_a dx_b}{R}. \tag{3.5}$$

Hence, for a non-ferromagnetic medium ($\mu = $ const) the induction law assumes the form

$$e = -\frac{\mu}{4\pi} \int_a \int_b \frac{dx_a dx_b}{R} \frac{di_a}{dt} = -M_{ab} \frac{di_a}{dt}, \tag{3.6}$$

where

M_{ab} — mutual inductance of the two circuits a and b,
μ — absolute magnetic permeability of the medium.

For the symmetry of the expression (3.5) it appears that the ϕ_{ab} flux, originating in b and permeating a is expressed by the formula

$$\phi_{ba} = M_{ab} i_b. \tag{3.7}$$

In case of a system of m circuits, through which alternating currents are flowing, the resultant electromotive force of mutual induction in each circuit n which results from the superposition of individual fluxes is therefore

$$e_n = -\sum_{k=1}^{m} M_{nk} \frac{di_k}{dt}. \tag{3.8}$$

The coefficient of mutual induction may be determined from general formula

$$M_{ab} = \frac{\mu}{4\pi} \oint \oint \frac{dx_a dx_b}{R} \cos\alpha, \tag{3.9}$$

where

x_a, x_b — length of the circuit elements a and b,
R — distance between the circuits,
α — angle between the elements of the circuits.

Let us calculate the coefficient of mutual induction of two conductors (sections) with lengths $l_a = l_b = l$ and with a radius r, positioned parallel, at a distance d (Fig. 3.1). Assuming $d \gg r$ and $l \gg r$, we can neglect the thickness of the cables and use the formula in the form of (3.6), i.e. (Fig. 3.1)

$$M_{ab} = \frac{\mu l}{4\pi} \int_0^{l_b} dx_b \int_0^{l_a} \frac{dx_a}{R} = \int_0^l \int_0^l \frac{dx_a dx_b}{\sqrt{d^2 + (x_b - x_a)^2}}. \tag{3.10}$$

After solving this we obtain the following formulas [17]:

$$M_{ab} = \frac{\mu l}{2\pi} \left[\ln \frac{l + \sqrt{l^2 + d^2}}{d} - \frac{\sqrt{l^2 + d^2} - d}{l} \right], \tag{3.11}$$

or

$$M_{ab} = \frac{\mu l}{2\pi} \left[\ln \left(\frac{l}{d} + \sqrt{\frac{l^2}{d^2} + 1} \right) - \sqrt{\frac{d^2}{l^2} + 1} + \frac{d}{l} \right]. \tag{3.12}$$

If we can assume that $l \gg d$, then, after transformation and reduction, we obtain

$$M_{ab} \approx \frac{\mu l}{2\pi} \left(\ln \frac{2l}{d} - 1 \right), \tag{3.13}$$

or

$$M_{ab} \approx \frac{\mu l}{2\pi} \ln \frac{l}{d}. \tag{3.14}$$

The choice of formula for calculating the mutual inductance of two parallel conductors depends on the accuracy of calculation required. However, the ratio of the length of the conductors l to their distance d is decisive. Thus for example, the approximate relative error, resulting from the use of the approximated formulas (3.13) or (3.14) is, respectively: for $l/d = 2$, an error of 100% or 10%; for $l/d = 10$, an error of 3.75% or -10%; for $l/d = 100$, an error of 0.233% or -6.55%; for $l/d = 1000$, an error of 0.016% or -4.35%. In practice, formula (3.13) is used most often.

The above relations were derived for linear circuits, but in practice they may also be used for conductors with a finite section, in view of the fact that the electromotive force of self-induction and the internal field are relatively insignificant.

If, however, the value of the current i induced in a supplementary conductor were high, one should add the electromotive force of self-induction in (3.6) and (3.8) formulas

$$e_s = -\frac{d(Li)}{dt} = -L\frac{di}{dt}.$$ (3.15)

For non-ferromagnetic media and for a constant current density throughout the entire section of the conductor (core) the self-inductance L depends only on the form and geometrical dimensions of the conductor. If we carry out calculations similar to those for the mutual inductance M for two conductors with finite sections, we obtain

$$L = \frac{\mu l}{2\pi}\left(\ln\frac{2l}{r} - \frac{3}{4}\right),$$ (3.16)

or

$$L \approx \frac{\mu l}{2\pi}\ln\frac{l}{r}.$$ (3.17)

3.3 Principles of calculating the induced voltages in the auxiliary cores of mining power cables

The power networks in underground mine workings are three-phase networks with insulated zero point (isolated neutral system). Multicore power cables—armoured cables and trailing cables and flexible conductors—are used for power supply, remote control and monitoring of mining equipment. According to the regulations in force, the protective earthing system also includes the auxiliary (complementary) cores (earth cores) which are bundled together with the power (main) cores in one, multicore cable.

The currents flowing through the power cores induce voltages (electromotive force) in the auxiliary (monitoring, control and protection) cores. Because of the very small distance d and the asymmetric positioning of cores inside the cable, the voltages may reach substantial values for cables feeding remote and heavy equipment. High transient voltages may be reached in cases of starting a cage motor, single-phase operation or a short-circuit, particularly in the case of a resistance type two-phase short-circuit.

Examples of the geometrical configurations of cores within the armoured power (traditional and new) cables and flexible mine cables most often used in Polish mines are presented in Figs. 3.2–3.7. In Figs. 3.2, 3.3 and 3.4 the power cores $L1, L2, L3$ are marked with the numbers 1, 2, 3, the protective (earth) core (PE) with 4, and the remaining cores with the numbers 5, 6, and 7.

In a three-phase symmetrical network, insulated relative to earth, the resultant electromotive force (E_p) induced in an auxiliary (earth, pilot)

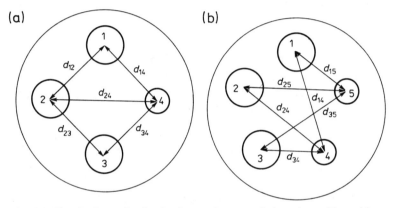

Fig. 3.2 Sketch of core distribution (eccentric—on a circle perimeter) in multicore mining cables: (a) 4-core, (b) 5-core

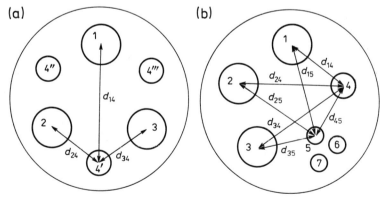

Fig. 3.3 Sketch of a geometric system of cores in cables: (a) 6-core, (b) 7-core

core P by the alternating currents $I_1,$* I_2, I_3 flowing in the power cores $L1$, $L2$, $L3$ may according to the general relation (3.8), be expressed as:

$$E_p = -M_{1p}\frac{dI_1}{dt} - M_{2p}\frac{dI_2}{dt} - M_{3p}\frac{dI_3}{dt}.$$ (3.18)

For a sinusoidal current with constant pulse $\omega = 2\pi f$, the mutual impedance Z_{ip} between the power (disturbing) circuit i and the complementary (disturbed) circuit p may be written as

$$Z_{ip} = j\omega M_{ip} = -\frac{E_p}{I_i},$$ (3.19)

where

M_{ip} — mutual inductance between the disturbing circuit i and the disturbed circuit p (relations (3.11) through (3.14)).

The cores of multicore mining cables may for practical purposes be treated as parallel conductors, while even for short segments $l \gg d$ (e.g. $\frac{l}{d} > 50$ already for $l = 1$ meter). The mutual inductance of each power core $L1$, $L2$, $L3$ relative to a complementary core P (e.g. protective unearthed core PU) may thus be calculated from formula (3.13). It is also assumed that the absolute magnetic permeability of the materials as fillers in mining cables, is practically equal to that of magnetic permeability of vacuum, i.e. $\mu = \mu_0 = 4\pi \cdot 10^{-7}$ Hm^{-1}.

For the case of symmetrical loading of power cores using the known relation $I_2 = a^2 I_1$, and $I_3 = a I_1$ substituting into (3.18) we obtain:

$$E_p = -\frac{dI_1}{dt}\left[M_{1p} + M_{2p}\left(-\frac{1}{2} - j\frac{\sqrt{3}}{2}\right) + \right.$$

$$\left. + M_{3p}\left(-\frac{1}{2} + j\frac{\sqrt{3}}{2}\right)\right].$$ (3.20)

After further substitution and calculations of the modulus we obtain a practical general formula for the r.m.s. voltage (r.m.s. electromotive force) induced in the complementary core relative to the r.m.s. value of

---

* Further in the text, symbols indicated as italic bold-face type denote complex numbers.

the symmetrical current of the power cores I and the geometrical system of cores in a cable (e.g. Figs. 3.2, 3.3, 3.4):

$$E_p = \mu_0 f I l_c \sqrt{\frac{1}{4}\left(\ln\frac{d_{1p}d_{1p}}{d_{2p}d_{3p}}\right)^2 + \frac{3}{4}\left(\ln\frac{d_{3p}}{d_{2p}}\right)^2} \quad [V], \qquad (3.21)$$

or

$$E_4 = \omega I l_c \sqrt{\left(\ln\frac{d_{14}d_{14}}{d_{24}d_{34}}\right)^2 + 3\left(\ln\frac{d_{34}}{d_{24}}\right)^2} \times 10^{-7} \quad [V], \qquad (3.22)$$

where

μ_0 — magnetic permeability of vacuum, H m^{-1},

$f = \dfrac{\omega}{2\pi}$ — current frequency, Hz,

I — current intensity in an power core, A,

l_c — core length in a cable of length l, m,

d_{ip} — distance between the axes of the corresponding power cores i and the axis of the complementary core p (protective core 4).

The length of the cores l_c ($l_c = kl$) depends on the true length of the cable l and the pitch h of the cores twisted among themselves into a helix on the axis or a central separator (elastomeric centre). For example, for flexible mining cables the length of the twist pitch h of power cores should not exceed a nine-fold multiple of its diameter $D(k = 1.005)$; for drilling cables, especially flexible ones, $h \geqslant 2.5\ D$ ($k \leqslant 1.08$). Hence, in practice, we can assume $l_c \approx l$.

The resultant electromotive force induced in the circuit constituted by two complementary cores, e.g. a protective (earth) core 4 and control (pilot) core 5 (Figs. 3.2b, 3.3, 3.4a) is calculated as the geometrical differences of electromotive forces induced in each complementary (auxiliary) core separately in the form

$$E_{45} = -(M_{14} - M_{15})\frac{dI_1}{dt} - (M_{24} - M_{25})\frac{dI_2}{dt} -$$

$$- (M_{34} - M_{35})\frac{dI_3}{dt}. \qquad (3.23)$$

(a)   (b)

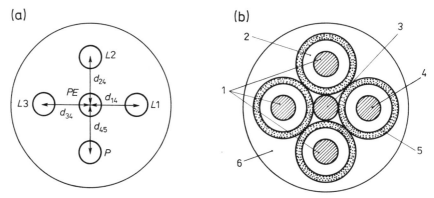

Fig. 3.4 Geometrical system of cores (YOGY, YOGYek) and the structural principle of a screened drilling machine cable of the YOGYek 5×4 mm^2 type 1 kV ($E'_4 \approx 0$): 1—working (power) cores, 2—PVC insulation, 3—bare earth, 4—pilot (auxiliary) core, 5—individual screens made of conducting polyethylene, 6—PVC outer sheath

After substituting the coefficients of mutual induction of the individual pairs of cores (formula (3.13)) and transformation, we obtain the equation for the effective value of the induced voltage:

$$E_{45} = \frac{1}{2} \mu f Il \sqrt{3 \left(\ln \frac{d_{35} d_{24}}{d_{34} d_{25}} \right)^2 + \left(\ln \frac{d_{14}^2 d_{25} d_{35}}{d_{15}^2 d_{24} d_{34}} \right)^2} \qquad (3.24)$$

or

$$E_{45} = \omega Il \sqrt{3 \left(\ln \frac{d_{35} d_{24}}{d_{34} d_{25}} \right)^2 + \left(\ln \frac{d_{14}^2 d_{25} d_{35}}{d_{15}^2 d_{24} d_{34}} \right)^2} \times 10^{-7}. \qquad (3.25)$$

Asymmetric loading of a line in a mine network may occur, first of all, in the case of a gap in one of the phases of a three-phase circuit. Then, in the two cores, currents flow, which have equal strength but opposite directions. In the case of a phase stoppage, e.g. $L3$ we have $I_2' = -(I_2 + I_3) = -(a^2 I_1 + a I_1) = -I_1$. The voltage induced in any core P of the cable and calculated as before will be

$$E_p = (M_{2p} - M_{1p}) \frac{dI_1}{dt} \qquad (3.26)$$

and

$$E_p = \mu_0 f Il \left(\ln \frac{d_{2p}}{d_{1p}} \right). \qquad (3.27)$$

Similarly, the voltage induced in a loop made of any two pilot cores of a multicore cable, e.g. of the earth core 4 and control core 5, can be determined and we obtain the formula

$$E_{45} = \mu_0 f Il \left(\ln \frac{d_{14}d_{25}}{d_{15}d_{24}} \right). \tag{3.28}$$

3.4 Values of voltages induced in the pilot (auxiliary) cores of power cables and flexible mining cables and methods of reducing them

The most effective method of reducing the electromagnetic interaction of an electromagnetic circuit with an auxiliary circuit is through appropriate design and the suitable distribution of cores in a multicore cable.

Asymmetric placement of auxiliary cores relative to the power cores reduces the resultant strength of the electromotive forces induces in them. Example of a partial symmetry are 4-, 5-, 6-, and 7-core cables, where the auxiliary cores are placed at a uniform distance d in relation to the two power cores (Fig. 3.2 and 3.3). In this case denoting $d_{1p} = d_{3p} = d_{min}$ (e.g. $d_{14} = d_{34} = d_{min}$) and $d_{2p} = d_{max}(d_{24} = d_{max})$, and $d_{15} = d_{34} = d_{min}$ and $d_{14} = d_{24} = d_{25} = d_{35} = d_{max}$, after substitution and appropriate transformation the formulas (3.22) and (3.25) assume the form

$$E_4 = 2\omega Il \times 10^{-7} \ln \frac{d_{max}}{d_{min}} \quad V \tag{3.29}$$

$$E_{45} = 2\sqrt{3}\,\omega Il \times 10^{-7} \ln \frac{d_{max}}{d_{min}} \quad V. \tag{3.30}$$

For a typical 4-core cable we can assume $\dfrac{d_{max}}{d_{min}}$ to be 1.41, whereas for a 5-core cable (Figs. 3.2b and 3.3b) $\dfrac{d_{max}}{d_{min}} = 1.62$. After substitution for $f = 50$ Hz and $l = 1000$ m we obtain for 4-core cables (Fig. 3.2a)

$$E_4 \approx 21.5 \cdot I \times 10^{-3} \quad V/km \tag{3.31}$$

or

$$E_4 = 21.5 \text{ mV/(A·km)},$$

and for five-core cables (Figs. 3.2b and 3.3b)

$$E_4 \approx E_5 \approx 30 \cdot I \times 10^{-3} \quad \text{V/km} \tag{3.32}$$

or

$$E_4 = E_5 \approx 30 \ \text{mV/(A·km)}$$

and

$$E_{45} \approx 52 \cdot I \times 10^{-3} \quad \text{V/km} \tag{3.33}$$

or

$$E_{45} \approx 52 \ \text{mV/(A·km)}.$$

Measurements carried out on various lengths of cables of the types OG, OnG and OnGek (4-, 5-, and 7-core cables with geometrical arrangements as presented in Figs. 3.2 and 3.3) showed [17, 18] that the measured values are on average some 10% (0–25%) higher than the values calculated from formulas (3.31)–(3.33).

An analysis of the formulas (3.21)–(3.24) and (3.29)–(3.30) shows that if there is full geometric symmetry of the auxiliary cores with respect to the power cores (e.g. when the pilot core is located in the middle between the power cores) we can reduce of the electromotive force of mutual induction to zero with a symmetrical load on the power cores. This

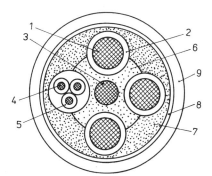

Fig. 3.5 The structure of a screened flexible mining cable of the OnGek type, 1 kV, 7-core (new design with an earth core in a central separator); $E'_4 = 2$–5 mV/(A·km), $E'_{45} = 25$ mV/(A·km), $E'_{56} \approx 0$: 1—power core, 2—rubber insulation of power core, 3—earth core, 4—pilot (auxiliary) core, 5—rubber insulation of pilot core, 6 and 7—central separator and conductive rubber covering, 8—cotton wrapping, 9—polychlorophrene outer sheath

solution has been used in the new Polish power cables and flexible mining cables (OnG, OnGek, YOGYek, YHKGXeky) which have the earth conductor with a reduced cross-section located directly along the axis of the cable (Figs. 3.4 and 3.7) or in the elastomeric cradle separator (e.g. Fig. 3.5). Another solution is to design an earth core consisting of three cores located as shown in Fig. 3.3a and galvanically joined with one another, e.g. the 6 kV flexible cables of the OGw (Fig. 3.6) or OnGbekż/w types. A similar result is obtained when the earth core is made of three conductive sheaths for each working core, joined with one another (e.g.

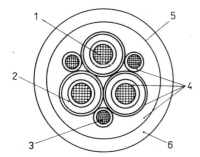

Fig. 3.6 The structure of a flexible cable of the OGw type (6 kV): 1—power cores, 2—butyl rubber insulation, 3—earth cores in conductive rubber, 4—sheaths and inserts made of conductive rubber (compensating and protective screens), 5—cotton band, 6—rubber outer sheath

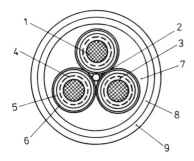

Fig. 3.7 Design principle of screened power mining cables of the YHKGXeky type: 1—power cores, 2—earth core (bare copper wire), 3—compensating (electric field) screen made of conductive polyethylene (in 6 kV cables only), 4—polyethylene insulation of working cores, 5—graphite tape (electric screen), 6—copper band wrapping (individual screens of the cores), 7—PVC filler, 8—copper band wrapping (general screen), 9—PVC covering

cables of the 3HKnFpy and 3HKYFpy types—Fig. 3.8) or it is made by
a common sheath (screen) around the cable core (Fig. 3.9). Measurements confirm that the voltages induced in the earth cores situated
geometrically in this way do not exceed a few mV/(A km) (examples of
the E' values measured for individual types of cables are given in the
description of Figures 3.4–3.8).

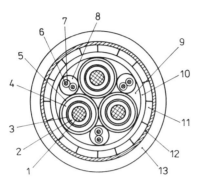

Fig. 3.8 The structure of a 6 kV screened cable of the 3HKnFpy and 3HKYFpy (3×35
         mm$^2 + 3 \times 2 \times 1.5$ mm^2) type [$E'_p = 55$ mV/(A·km); in lead sheath of one power
         core $E' = 70$ mV/(A·km); in three lead sheaths $E' = 8$ mV/(A·km)]: 1—power
         core, 2—paper or PVC insulation, 3—screen made of conductive paper or
         polyethylene, 4—lead sheath, 5—wrapping, 6—pilot core, 7 and 8—insulation
         and PVC covering of pilot cores, 9—filling, 10—PVC covering, 11—armouring
         made of flat steel wires, 12—reverse spiral casing, 13—anticorrosive covering
         made of PVC

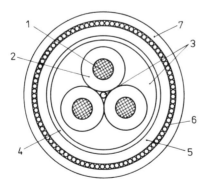

Fig. 3.9 The structure of a power mining cable 6 kV of the YKGYFoy (YKGYFty,
         YKGYFpy) type: 1—power core, 2—PVC insulation, 3—PVC filling, 4—copper
         band wrapping (earth core), 5—PVC covering, 6—steel armouring, 7—PVC tube

Thus we are left with the problem of reducing the effects of electromagnetic interaction onto a circuit consisting of two auxiliary (e.g. pilot) cores.

It appears from an analysis of formula (3.24) that a substantial decrease of the value of the electromotive force induced in a pair of pilot cores (e.g. 5 and 6 in Fig. 3.3b), located in a magnetic field, is possible when

$$\frac{d_{16}}{d_{15}} = \frac{d_{26}}{d_{25}} = \frac{d_{36}}{d_{35}} \approx 1.$$

This can be obtained as a result of an appropriately frequent transposition of pilot (auxiliary) cores along the entire length of the cable. This arrangement is used in e.g. Polish 7-core flexible mining cables (Fig. 3.5). Three pilot cores (5, 6 and 7—Fig. 3.3b) of this cable are additionally twisted with the pitch h_p, which is much smaller than the pitch h of the twist of the main cores. This structure causes an approximately similar mean distance between all the pilot cores and the power cores. A detailed analysis of the problem reveals [37] that the transposition of the pilot cores results in a reduction of the induced electromotive force (EMF) by a factor of $2l/h_p$. If we assume, for example, that $h_p = 0.1$ m for a cable of 1 m length, the EMF is already reduced by 20 times. In measurements carried out on an OnG 4×25 mm$^2 + 3 \times 2.5$ mm^2 cable of 27 m length, a value of $E'_{56} = 1$ mV/(A km) was obtained.

The induced electromotive forces cause the flow of stray currents in closed circuits: in the circuits directly subjected to the interaction of the fields (e.g. in control circuits) or in exterior circuits (e.g. in earth return circuits). In this way additional sources are being formed, with a relatively low internal resistance and with the power of a few tens of watts. These may constitute real hazards, e.g. irregular operation of control systems, loss of intrinsic safety, dangerous heating, etc., since we should remember that in a case of high current flow (e.g. during the starting of mining equipment) additional voltages of less than twenty volts appear in the circuit made up of the earth and pilot cores of a flexible cable, and therefore also currents with amplitudes of at least a few amperes.

The frequency and the shape of the curve of the induced voltage correspond to that of the currents in the power cores. The current in the power core most distant from the pilot cores is decisive. At different combinations of the order of phases, the voltages induced may be shifted by from 0 to $(5/3)\pi$ relative to the supply voltage of the auxiliary circuit (e.g. of a control system). The resultant voltage in the circuit is made up of the sum (difference) of the induced and supply (auxiliary) voltages. The greatest resultant of the current in the circuit will occur in the case of a consistent flow of induced and "supply" currents (the interference and operative "signals" will add up): otherwise the currents are subtracted (the induced interference signal weakens the operative signal). In practice this could cause, for example, the spontaneous starting or switching off of equipment (e.g. of a conveyor during the starting of a coal shearer) or difficulties in switching on the machines. This depends on the logic used in the design of the control and monitoring systems. A reduction of hazards of this type can be obtained by improving the construction of flexible cables: mostly by using a symmetrical geometrical cable design, i.e. by changing the position of the earth core (e.g. along the axis of the cable—Figs. 3.4, 3.5, 3.7, or as a sheath on the cable core—Fig. 3.9) and control (pilot—e.g. Fig. 3.8) cores in relation to working (power) cores. However, a radical improvement can be obtained simultaneously by using appropriate modifications of the entire system of control and monitoring including for example abandoning the use of an earthed pilot core for control circuits. In this case the use of pilot cores bundled into one cable ("core" of a flexible cable) with an appropriately small length of the pitch h_p will allow the influence of induced interferences (voltages) to be reduced to minimum.

3.5   The influence of screens used in power cables and flexible mining cables

Screens used in flexible cables and conductors feeding present power networks are made of non-magnetic conductive materials. These materials include copper, aluminium, lead, metallized or carbonized paper and conductive rubber, PCV or polyethylene. The absolute magnetic permeability of these materials is practically equal to the permeability of a vacuum μ_0.

Examples of the structure of screened flexible mining cables and power cables are presented in Figs. 3.4–3.8. The principal task of these screens is electric protection; protection against interphase internal short-circuits and reduction of the effects of external mechanical damages as well as protection against "taking out" the working (on-load) voltage of the cable. In high-voltage cables, the task of individual screens around power cores is also to improve the distribution (uniformity) of the electric field. All these tasks are being fulfilled satisfactorily by the screens used.

To evaluate the influence of screens in limiting the electromagnetic interaction of a magnetic field as well, we have to make an analysis of the propagation of a sinusoidal plane wave in a medium with an electric permeability ε and a conductivity γ, for which the complex electric permeability ε_c is given by:

$$\varepsilon_c = \varepsilon - j\frac{\gamma}{\omega}. \tag{3.34}$$

From the system of Maxwell's equations we obtain a attenuation wave, whose amplitude decreases exponentially, as the attenuation coefficient α. The source of the attenuation lies in the dispersion of energy in the conductivity γ of the medium. At the depth $p = 1/\alpha$ the wave is being suppressed by a factor of 2.7183 (the coefficient p is called a *penetration depth*, and it may be assumed to be an indicator of the speed of wave collapse).

In an insulating medium $\gamma/\omega \ll \varepsilon$ and the conduction current γK may be disregarded as it is insignificant compared to the displacement current of amplitude $\omega\varepsilon K$, whereas in a conductive medium $(\gamma/\omega \gg \varepsilon)$ the displacement current is usually disregarded as being weak compared to the conduction current.

During the transition from insulation to screen, part of the energy of a plane wave perpendicular to the conductive plane (screen) is reflected, while part of it enters the screen and is transformed into an attenuation wave and gradually disappears (energy dispersion in medium). The condition for the absence of reflection is that of the equality of the wave impedance of the insulation medium Z_i and the conductive medium Z_s, where

$$Z_i = \sqrt{\frac{\mu}{\varepsilon}}, \tag{3.35a}$$

$$Z_s = \sqrt{\frac{\omega\mu}{\gamma}}. \tag{3.35b}$$

The wave length λ and the attenuation coefficient α in both mediums (i in insulation, s in screen) may be calculated from the relationships:

$$\lambda_i = \frac{1}{f\sqrt{\mu\varepsilon}} = \frac{\lambda_0}{\sqrt{\varepsilon_r\mu_r}}, \tag{3.36a}$$

$$\lambda_s = \frac{2\pi}{\sqrt{\pi\mu\gamma f}}, \tag{3.36b}$$

$$\alpha_i = \frac{1}{2}\gamma\sqrt{\frac{\mu}{\varepsilon}}, \tag{3.37a}$$

$$\alpha_s = \sqrt{\pi\mu\gamma f}. \tag{3.37b}$$

From an analysis of these relationships it follows that apart from the case of a very high frequency only a screen with a very high conductivity ($\gamma \to \infty$), does not permeate the wave and thus effectively eliminates electromagnetic interaction. We may assume that, in a conductor, the wave practically already disappears at a depth 2–3 times smaller than the wavelength. For eample it has been calculated that for a frequency $f = 50$ Hz the wavelength λ_s and the depth of penetration p_s are the following: for copper $\lambda_s = 60.5$ mm, $p_s = 9.65$ mm; for aluminium $\lambda_s = 76.5$ mm, $p_s = 12.2$ mm; for lead $\lambda_s = 208$ mm, $p_s = 33$ mm; conductive rubber ($\gamma = 0.1$ S/m) $\lambda_s = 1420$ m, $p_s = 226$ m. It can be seen that these types of screens have practically no influence upon the values of electromotive forces induced in pilot cores of power cables. This is fully confirmed by measurements carried out on screened cables with designs as presented in Figs. 3.4–3.8.

If individual screens on working (power) cores (e.g. metal screens—Figs. 3.7 and 3.8) are not shorted to one another, and the load on the working cores is symmetrical, then the electromotive force E_{sy} induced in the screen can be calculated from the general formula (3.22), e.g. in the form of (3.29); in this formula d_{min} is the radius of the screen (as measured from the centre of its thickness). If the screens are shorted at both ends or possibly earthed at one end only, the geometrical sum of currents in screens as well as the resultants of voltage are practically equal to zero.

Attention should also be paid to the important influence of an iron screen, even in the form of an armouring of steel tape or wires used for wrapping insulated mining cables, which can occur in practice. If we consider that, for iron ($\mu = 4\pi \times 10^{-4}$ H/m, $\gamma = 0.8 \times 10^7$ S/m) $\lambda = 5$ mm, $p = 0.795$ mm, we can assume that the electromagnetic interaction in the vicinity of such cables is negligible. In the case of unarmoured cables, this condition can only be assumed in relation to the interactions (of field intensity) induced by high frequency harmonics.

The problem of induction of interference voltages in machine operation control and monitoring circuits, their possible effects (potential hazards) and the possibilities of reducing their influence is discussed, for example, of Polish designs of power cables and flexible mining cables. However, the general principles of analysis, methods of calculation and conclusions drawn can also be used for cable designs used in other countries. Thus for example the cable designs presented in Figs. 3.4 and 3.9 correspond to the flexible cables of types 7 and 20 made in Great Britain (BICC); those in Fig. 3.5 to GRSz and RKP made in the USSR; those in Figs. 3.3b, 3.6 and 3.8 to NSSHöu, NSSHcbEöu and NTSCgE-RLöu made in Germany.

3.6   The influence of the operation of thyristor converters on interference in high-voltage power networks

Power supplies with controlled semiconductors rectifiers are used in underground mines mainly in drive systems of winding equipment and of trolley and storage-battery driven locomotives. With regard to high-power values (a few MW), the interference due to the supply systems winding machine shall be discussed first. Here it is common practice to use two series-connected, controlled rectifiers, supplied from transformers with different connection groups (Dy, Dd) resulting in a 12-pulse rectification.

We can assume that the currents i supplied to the rectifiers are of rectangular shape with a maximum value (amplitude) I_m. Then the spectrum of the alternating current absorbed from the power network with pulsation ω has the form [30]:

$$i = \frac{4\sqrt{3}}{\pi} I_m (\cos \omega t - \frac{1}{11} \cos 11 \omega t + \frac{1}{13} \cos 13 \omega t - \frac{1}{23} \cos 23 \omega t +$$

$$+ \frac{1}{25} \cos 25 \omega t + ...). \tag{3.38}$$

Therefore, in the current absorbed by the 12-pulse system, there occur harmonics called *characteristic harmonics*, i.e. of the $12n \pm 1$-order. It should be noted however, that equation (3.38) is a simplification of reality, as the influence of commutation and voltage drops in the supply network have been neglected.

The harmonics of the current absorbed by a rectifier produce voltage harmonics in the supply network.

Actual measurements reveal that in the voltage of a 6 kV network, supplying a winding machine "with a thyristor drive", there occur characteristic (time variable) harmonics which depend on the operating conditions of the winding machine (start-up, constant driving speed, braking). An example of this variability [30] is presented in Fig. 3.10.

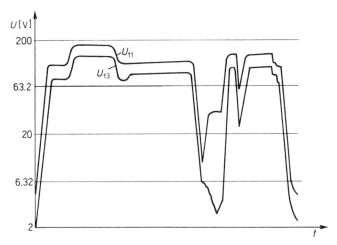

Fig. 3.10 The 11th and 13th harmonics in the 6 kV supply voltage for thyristor winding machine in function of time

This figure reveals that for a constant operating speed the voltage harmonics do not vary with time; the values of the characteristic harmonics measured in this circuit are the following: 550 Hz—160 V, 650 Hz—140 V, 1150 Hz—127 V, 1250 Hz—100 V. The measurements also reveal the occurrence of other (non-characteristic) harmonics, but their amplitudes do not depend on the operating conditions of a winding machine; they do not originate in converters in the system of a winding machine.

Thyristor converters are also the source of pulse interference. Figure 3.11 presents an example of voltage variations in the network supplying a three-phase, full-wave rectifier loaded with 500 kW (380 V) motor; the r.m.s. value of the current drawn from the supply network was 100 A [43]. The amplitude of the pulses shown in the figure depends on the firing angle of the thyristor and the value of the converter supply voltage. The strength of the load current and its nature have little influence upon the amplitude but the time of pulse duration depends on them; the pulse-rise-time is of the order of 1 μs [43].

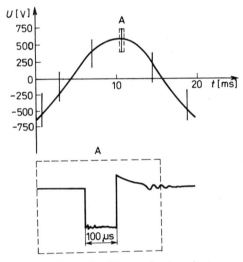

Fig. 3.11 Example of line noting transient generated by static power converter

Example of the characteristics of the intensity interference voltages, generated by a thyristor rectifier are given in Fig. 3.12 [43] in band form (the larger voltage values correspond to larger values of the firing angle).

For the purpose of designing (or selecting) thyristor converters with current enforcement (supplied from 110 kV network) the generalized results of investigations conducted to date can be used as a guide. To assess voltage distortions one should take the values of the higher harmonics in the primary current of fully controlled bridge converters with the pulse number $p = 6$ or 12—Table 3.1. It is also assumed as a simplification that these do not vary during the entire operation period (e.g. in the output cycle of a winding machine). In reality, however, even the supply voltage reveals a certain primary content of higher harmonics, whilst the individual elements that make up the converters also differ from one another (e.g. allowable tolerances). The result of these facts among others, is that in the case of 12-pulse bridge converters, there occur remnant values of odd harmonics, characteristic of 6-pulse interaction (i.e. 5, 7, 17, 19). Other higher harmonics, e.g. even or triple (multiple of three) do also occur in the converter current.

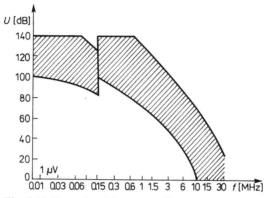

Fig. 3.12 Example of frequency characteristics of interference voltage in the network supplying a controlled rectifier

TABLE 3.1   Percentage values of the n-th higher harmonics in the current of 6- and 12-pulse, fully-controlled converters

n	5	7	11	13	17	19	23	25
$p = 6$	19.5	13.5	8.0	6.0	4.0	3.0	2.0	1.5
$p = 12$	2.0	1.0	8.0	6.0	0.5	0.5	2.0	1.5

In investigations carried out on the Polish 2L-6000 winding machines (2 DC motors of 2000 kW), even harmonics, mostly of the orders: $n = 2$, 4, 6, 8, 10, have been found to occur on the side of 6 kV converter transformers. The highest percentage content of harmonic was: in the current 15% for $n = 2$; 18.1% for $n = 4$; 10.6% for $n = 8$; 5.2% for $n = 10$; 1.6% for $n = 12$; 2.1% for $n = 20$; and in voltage: 3.4% for $n = 2$; 4% for $n = 4$; 9% for $n = 8$; 2.2% for $n = 16$. Thus, the primary currents are not symmetrical relatives to the time axis. One of the reasons for this lies in the large variations in the characteristics of individual thyristors, which cause non-uniform loading of individual bridge branches. Therefore, in the design and assembly of bridge systems the elements (thyristor tolerances) should be appropriately grouped.

Pulse interferences produced by converters are distributed throughout the supply network, and are suppressed in lines (primarily cable lines) and in transformers. An example of the propagation of interference pulses produced by the thyristor exciter of a generator is presented in Fig. 3.13 [43]. Mean values of the insertion loss of power transformers are: 10–20 dB for unscreened windings, 15–30 dB for screened windings, and 0.06 dB/m for cable lines.

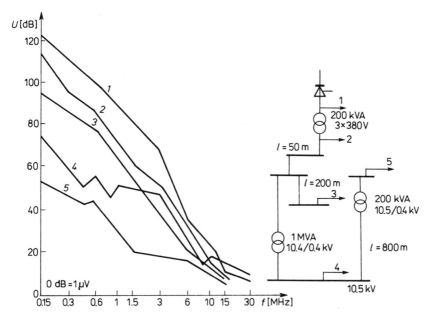

Fig. 3.13 Example of interference pulse propagation, produced by a thyristor exciter; results of measurements at the points 1–5

In deep mines with separate supplies for underground and hoisting practically no electromagnetic interference originating in the converter drives of winding machines has been found in underground networks.

3.7   Examples of the results of measurements of electromagnetic interference in underground low-voltage networks and their immediate vicinity

In these networks and their direct vicinity, besides the parasitic voltages, sinusoidal with a frequency of 50 Hz, induced in auxiliary circuits, discussed in Section 3.4, there also occur other electromagnetic interferences. First of all mention should be made of the harmonics of voltages, currents, and electromagnetic fields, induced by the presence of non-linear elements in a power system and by the transient states due to the switching and the randomly alternating load of mining machines. The amplitudes and frequencies of harmonic voltages depend, in general, on the number of devices, the power of the receivers and the extent of the

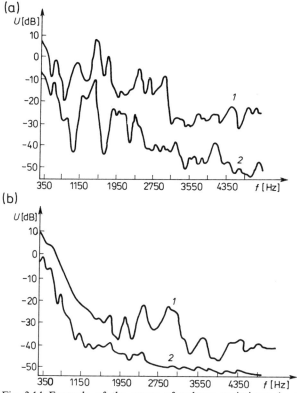

Fig. 3.14 Example of the range of voltage variations: 1—greatest and 2—smallest harmonic voltages of interference in the mines with a large (a) and small (b) installed power of electrical equipment (0 dB = 0.775 V)

network. Figure 3.14 presents for example the generalized results (maximum (curve 1—Fig. 3.14) and minimum (curve 2—Fig. 3.14) levels of harmonics (U)) of experiments carried out in the USSR on the 380 V networks of mines with a "high" (a) and a "low" (b) installed power [13]. Figure 3.15 also presents the frequency characteristics of interference voltages, which illustrate the influence of switching on and off a three-phase squirrel-cage motor [5].

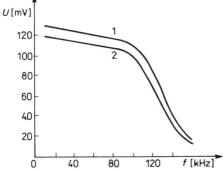

Fig. 3.15 Example of the frequency characteristics of pulse interference voltages: 1—during switching on and 2—switching off an asynchronous, squirrel-cage motor

Measurements of interference voltages and currents, which occur in terminal low-voltage networks, were carried out in a 500 V network presented schematically in Fig. 3.16. Measurements of the harmonics of the in-phase voltage were carried out in a system as presented in Fig. 3.17, whereas Fig. 3.18 illustrates the system used for measuring in cable currents.

The protective capacitor C_0 and resistor R_0 (Fig. 3.17) were selected according to the recommendations given in PN-75/E-08003; the resistance R_p, across which the interference voltages were measured according to PN-68/T-04502 was: 150 Ω for the frequency range up to 30 MHz and 75 Ω for 30 to 300 MHz. Voltages were measured with a selective nanovoltmeter (Unipan-233) with an active 50 Hz filter (high-pass filter, attenuation for 50 Hz—48 dB) in the first (I) frequency range (0.2–10 kHz) and with selective interference meters (NLMZ-4, LMZ-4, ULMZ-4) in the second (II) frequency range (10 kHz–100 MHz). The results of the measurements are presented as an example in Fig. 3.19. The same meters and laboratory transformers IL-4 were used to measure the values of current harmonics (Fig. 3.18); the results are given in Fig. 3.20.

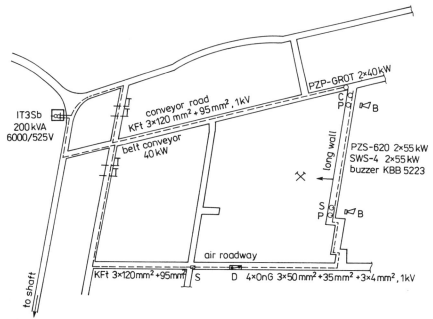

Fig. 3.16 Simplified map of mine workings and the distribution of electric equipment of
the 500 V network investigated: *P*, *C*—electric motors driving a plow and face
conveyor, *B*—signal buzzer (howler), *S*—main switch of supply for longwall
equipment, *D*—point of installation of measuring equipment

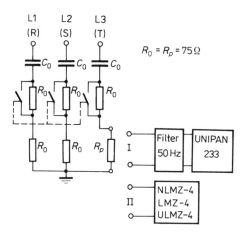

Fig. 3.17 Schematic system of measuring the asymmetric interference voltage

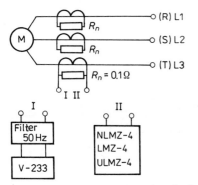

Fig. 3.18 Principle of measuring the interference current

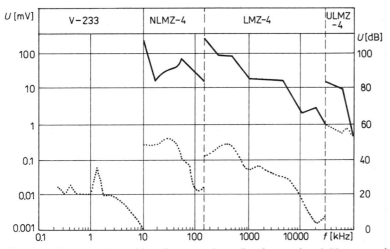

Fig. 3.19 Highest values of interference voltage (in phase voltage) U measured in the individual frequency bands f: —— receivers (plow, conveyor) on, ... receivers off

Taking advantage of the fact that the interference meters were with loop measuring antennas, measurements of the intensity of electromagnetic interference field "close" to the 500 V power lines, supplying the devices installed at a longwall (SWS-4 plow, PZS-620 scraper conveyor; Fig. 3.16), were carried out. These measurements were conducted for various operating conditions (motor start-up and switching-off, machine operation with variable load) and while connecting electric howler (KBB-5223). The results of the measurements are presented in Fig. 3.21.

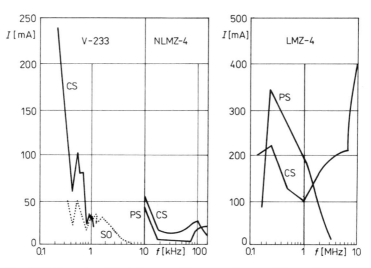

Fig. 3.20 Example of the influence of the operating conditions of longwall machines on the value of interference in the in-phase current: CS—conveyor start, PS—plow start, SO—stable operation

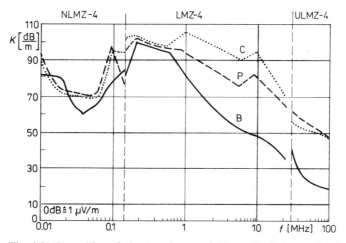

Fig. 3.21 Intensities of the interference fields K (0 dB = 1 μV/m) in the immediate surroundings of flexible mining cables supplying (Fig. 3.16): plow P, conveyor C and buzzer B

They show the peak values of the interference field intensity, measured using a frame antenna, to be located directly (the distance between the centre of the loop antenna and the cable was some tens of centimetres) under the flexible cables supplying the motor of the plow P and of conveyor C as well as those of the howler B. The measurements carried out reveal, among others, that up to a frequency of 10 kHz the harmonics of the phase voltages and currents in a low-voltage network have a linear spectrum. For frequencies above 10 kHz, due to the selectivity of interference meters, the spectrum is continuous, and the source of interference is constituted by transient states induced by switching the machines on and off, as well as the variability of their loading. For in-phase voltages, the occurrence of interference voltages with values up to 0.2 V were found over a broad range of frequencies. The differences in the measurements carried out for the plow and conveyor did not exceed 10 dB; variations in the results of measurements of the same values carried out with two meters for similar frequencies (150 kHz and 30 MHz) are due to the different widths of the carrier bands between individual interference meters. The influence of the mode of operation of the machines on the values of current harmonics was negligible; for the higher frequencies (above 10 kHz) the occurrence of interference currents was noticed only during the starting-up of the motors.

A substantial increase in the interference level in power and communication networks should be expected if thyristor converters are introduced into the drives of (face) mining machines. This can be confirmed by the results of laboratory measurements of inter-ferences produced by an inverter station (TZ-1) supplying the tractor of a coal drum shearer (KGS-150). The thyristor feeder (inverter) makes it possible to adjust the speed of the tractor by changing the frequency of the voltage feeding its electric motor. A schematic diagram of the measuring system is presented in Fig. 3.22. The inverter station (IS) supplied the asynchronous motor mechanically coupled with

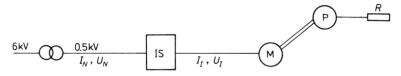

Fig. 3.22 The test set-up for investigating the inverter station: M—asynchronous motor, P—DC generator

a DC generator (load). The variable resistance of the generator load
(R) made it possible to adjust the load of the inverter station.
The current I_I and the voltage U_I at the output of the inverter station
and the current I_N in the network feeding the inverter station was
substantially distorted, as shown in Fig. 3.23. The values of the
harmonics of the U_I voltage and I_I current depend on the load of the
inverter station and on the output frequency. For example, for an
inverter output frequency $f_I = 50$ Hz, the relative value of harmonics,
relative to the first one (50 Hz), was in the U_I voltage: $U_3 = 22\%$,

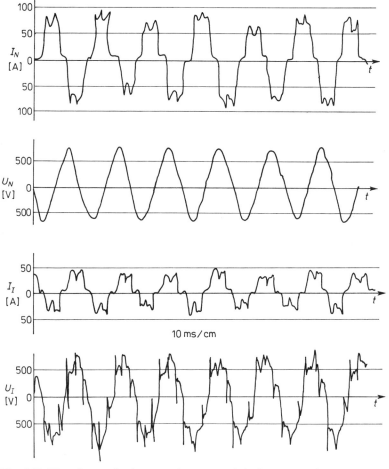

Fig. 3.23 Wave forms of voltages and currents of the inverter station

$U_6 = 4.1\%$, $U_9 = 7.8\%$, whereas for the frequency $f_I = 30$ Hz, the fraction of harmonics in the I_I current calculated in a similar way was, e.g.: $I_3 = 47\%$, $I_7 = 40\%$, $I_{11} = 40\%$, $I_{23} = 6.7\%$. These values were obtained for the inverter with the motor of the shearer tractor running, and loaded with 35 kW.

The interaction of an inverter station with communications systems depends on the value of an unbalanced component of the current I_{nb} in the cable connecting the inverter station with the motor. The unbalanced component of the current is constituted by the geometrical sum of the currents flowing in the working (power) cores, the earth core, and control (pilot) cores of the cable. Results of the measurements of the I_{nb} component carried out with a current transformer are presented in Table 3.2.

TABLE 3.2   Results of the measurements of the unbalanced component of current — for a motor at idle run
(I_{nb}) and after loading (I_{nbl})

f [kHz]	I_{nb} [mA]	I_{nbl} [mA]
10	16–26	3–3.6
20	4–5.3	3.7
100	0.6–1.2	0.3
150	0.3–0.4	0.14

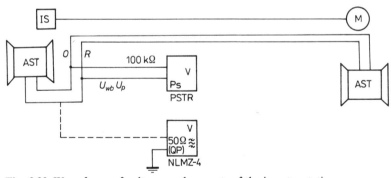

Fig. 3.23 Wave forms of voltages and currents of the inverter station

At a coal face, the cable connecting an inverter station with the tractor drive motor is placed in locks, parallel to the cable for loudspeaking (communication system) devices. That is why measurements of the interference voltages produced in the loudspeaking device cable by inverter station were also carried out. The r.m.s. value in the interference voltage U_{wb} and the psophometric interference voltage of U_p were measured: a diagram of the measuring system is presented in Fig. 3.24. The presence of interference voltages with values $U_{wb} = 4.4$ mV and $U_p = 2.4$ mV was confirmed, even in the case where only the master controller of the inverter station was operating. When operating the station loaded with the shearer motor, the interference voltage values were: $U_{wb} = 9$ mV, $U_p = 7$ mV.

4 Sources and Propagation of Electromagnetic Interference in Electric Traction Networks

4.1 Preliminary remarks

In electric traction networks direct ("rectified") current is used most often. Currently the use of thyristor converters in mining traction networks is increasing as well. The principal components of an underground electric traction network that produce electromagnetic interference, are rectifier stations, trolley locomotives, and contact wire and storage-battery locomotives. For example, a 6-pulse current rectification in a rectifier station, with no interference eliminators, causes interference not only in the immediate vicinity of the station, but also in the components of alternating currents and voltages along traction lines, propagating even to remote workings. Peak values of voltage harmonics typically lie within the limits of 10 V for 300 Hz to 1 V for 1800 Hz, whereas the values of current intensity harmonics are, for example, 10 A for 300 Hz and 500 mA for 1800 Hz.

The introduction of converter systems in mining traction equipment, which makes it possible to adjust the speed, smoothly and economically, has resulted in an increase of electromagnetic interference. In locomotives, instead of resistance starters, thyristor choppers are being introduced. At loading and unloading stations, a supply from mobile thyristor stations (APST) is used since this allow smooth changes at low speeds.

Electric traction lines are usually composed of one or a few bar conductors suspended in the air (the so-called *overhead network*, contact wire) and steel railway tracks (rails) laid on special sleepers on the ground surface (floor). These tracks together with their connections and possible additional cables constitute the so-called *return circuit*.

The variation in operating conditions of a traction system (no-load state, working state proper, interference state) produces electromagnetic interactions, which can be the cause of interference. Around the wires of a traction line, there exists an electromagnetic field. The electric component of this field, induced by the difference in potentials between the overhead (contact) wire and the rails (earth), is the cause of electric interaction (capacitative-voltaic coupling). The magnetic component of the field, produced by the flow of current in the overhead (contact) wire and in the rails and the earth (rock) is the source of magnetic interaction (inductive-current coupling). These interactions may produce various effects. In neighbouring communications circuits, for example, stray voltages may be produced which may be sufficiently high to pose a hazard to the personnel and which also lower the quality of transmissions by causing the deformation of transmitted signals. Therefore, in practice, we should first of all analyse a system consisting of two circuits: a two-wire traction circuit (the contact wire), which usually is the source of the interference and a communications circuit, which usually is the receiver of the interference (interfered object). In these systems, and particularly under the specific conditions of operation of mine traction equipment, the earth (return) circuit may substantially influence the electromagnetic interactions and their effects. The influence of the return circuit is particularly well seen in mining working and in those cases where the circuits are connected to the earth (earthened), both for the circuit emitting and receiving the interference.

Stray currents with values over 1 A, and even exceeding 20 A, may serve as one of the examples of unwanted electrical interactions resulting from the use of electrical traction. These are, first of all, galvanic interactions, but in many cases they may be electromagnetic ones [18]. The problem of stray currents will not be analysed in detail in the remainder of the present work, therefore it seems advisable to discuss it briefly here.

Characteristics of the causes and sources of stray currents
Electric currents flowing along different paths, in the earth (in the soil, in the rock) and in conductive materials (e.g. metallic objects) which do not constitute the elements of a purpose-built electric circuit, are called *stray currents*. The "internal" paths of stray current flow are characterized by certain electric resistances of which produces voltage drops. In this

approach, the "source" of a stray current, which can occur in any external circuit, is constituted by any two points along such an internal path between which there occurs the difference in potential U_0, and with which the external circuit may make contact. These are low-power sources; in a substitute diagram they usually are represented by the difference of potentials U_0 and an internal resistance Z_i (usually the effective resistance R_i). The voltage drop U in the external circuit connected to the "source" of the stray current is called the *stray voltage*. The external circuit may be a real circuit, specifically intended for electric current flow (e.g. short circuit, control circuit, measurement circuit) or an undesirable circuit (made accidentally, e.g. at the point of contact between the structures of a shearer and conveyor) which represents a certain hazard (e.g. explosion, fire, corrosion).

The principal reason for the occurrence of stray currents is the technological activity of man in certain environment. From this broad generalized causes, the following of all more specific ones should be mentioned first as constituting potential hazards in mining:

— trolley electric traction on a given level or on a neighbouring level,
— electrified tram or railway lines,
— electric welding equipment,
— high- and low-voltage AC power networks (particularly in interference conditions),
— communication networks, control and warning circuits,
— means of communication using radio transmitters.

Other causes may also be of importance. They include:

— local galvanic cells, which are formed as a result of the presence of metallic masses in wet compartments with high-grade mineralization and water (moisture) occurrig together,
— static electricity,

and occasionally extra-technological causes, such as:

— atmospheric discharges,
— spontaneous polarization fields,
— natural earth current fields (telluric fields, fields resulting from changes in the earth's magnetic field).

The range of dangerous or unwanted interactions of stray currents under favourable conditions (environment) is much broader than is generally recognized. In the most general case, the presence of stray currents, particularly in underground excavations, may produce the following:

- hazards during blasting—possible accidental firing of the detonator due to a stray current of appropriate strength entering the circuit,
- risk of explosion as a result of sparking, which can occur when two bodies under stray voltage make contact or resulting from stray voltages in intrinsically safe circuits,
- fire danger as a result of the long-lasting flow of a stray current, resulting in the ignition of a coal dust or methane due to local heating up to the ignition temperature,
- hazards to personnel or reduced production due to the failure of control systems and disturbances caused by the penetration of stray current (and stray voltages) into the control, monitoring and warning circuits of mining equipment and devices,
- other hazards and losses due to corrosion damage to equipment and devices as well as to elements of protection and control systems.

A knowledge of the true sources of stray currents and the hazards posed by their interaction is indispensable, particularly in prophylactic action. Theoretically, most of the listed causes and possible effects may occur simultaneously. Usually, however, in local mining practice, some of the causes and effects may be neglected or their influence assumed to be restricted both in space and time.

Current leakage from electric traction systems (rails) constitutes the major and most frequent cause of the induction of strong stray currents. In a mine, the occurrence of stray currents may be caused by the operation of electric traction networks on the level under consideration, on other levels, or even on the surface.

Traffic rails constitute a substantial element of the traction network, as, together with the additional compensation wires, they constitute the return line for the current used up by traction equipment. The rails, as a part of the electric circuit, are represented in the substitute diagram by two parameters: longitudinal resistance (R_l) and transverse (earth) resistance (R_t). In the analysis of practical cases it is assumed that both resistances are uniformly distributed along the entire length of the rails (uniform circuit), i.e.:

$$R_l = r_l l,$$

$$R_t = \frac{r_t}{l},$$

where

r_l—longitudinal resistance of the rails per unit length $[\Omega/m]$,

r_t—resistance of leakage from the rails to earth, per unit length $[\Omega \cdot m]$,

l—length of the rails (track) $[m]$.

From the point of view of the possibility of the formation of stray currents, the rails are characterized by the so-called *leakage coefficient* α, which is determined from the expression

$$\alpha = \sqrt{\frac{r_l}{r_t}} \quad [m^{-1}].$$

As a result of the difference in potential between the rails and the roadbed (floor), part of the current leaks from the rails, flows through the "earth" and returns back to the rails. This part of the circuit in which the rails are positive relative to the neutral earth, is called the *anode zone*. In general the distribution of anode and cathode zones varies in time and depends on the method (place) of feeding the traction line and the location of the locomotives. Unloaded lengths of rails (the length between the locomotive and the end of the track) belong entirely to the anode zone or cathode zone (the length between the feeding station and the end of the track); hence they substantially influence the formation of stray currents. The total strength of stray currents induced by the operation of a given length of an electric traction network is equal to the difference between the load current of the feeder of the rectifier station feeding this length and the current in the rails at the point separating the anode and cathode zones.The intensity of stray currents (leak from the rails) increases when:

— the voltage drop within the rails increases, which produces an increase in the difference between the potentials of the rails and the earth,

— the resistance of the rails increases relative to the resistance of the leakage to the earth (leakage coefficient α).

In practice, the following factors are decisive:

— the lay-out of the traction network and the distribution of feeding
  stations,
— the location of the locomotives and the amount of current
  consumed,
— the condition of the rails and the roadbed.

The optimum situation is that of feeding from a few traction stations
(rectifier) distributed at equal distances along the line; the total strength
of stray currents may then be 3 to 4 times lower than in the case of feeding
from a single station [18].

The strength of stray currents increases in the following cases:
— with an increase in the line load currents (directly proportional)
  and of the length of the line,
— with the receivers (locomotives) moving away from the feeding
  station,
— with an increase of the leakage coefficient (use of lighter rails,
  improper longitudinal connectors, lack of ballast and wet roadbed).

Particularly unfavourable conditions occur during the starting-up of the
locomotives, due to the variable and high current consumption.
Increases in voltage drops are also caused by inter-rail connections being
faulty or absent. An increase in the longitudinal rail resistance to leakage
resistance ratio occurs particularly in the case of rails being covered with
concrete, laying the rails on a wet roadbed or when they are flooded with
water.

In well designed and mantained rails, the voltage drop (ΔU) does not
exceed 20 V; in this case about 50% of the current flows through the rails.
However, there are cases, when $\Delta U = 80$ V; then at the most only small
percentage of the load current flows through the rails; the rest returns
through the earth as stray currents.

Electrified lines of cable traction networks on the surface of the earth,
running through the area of a mine or in its vicinity may also produce of
stray currents, even at relatively deep levels of both underground and
open-cast mines. This is due to the fact that current leakage from the rails
of cable (trolley) produces a very extensive electric current field; the
extend of this field depends mainly on the previously discussed
characteristic features of traction networks (method of feeding, value of
load current, length and cross-sections of lines, the way of laying and
connecting the rails, preservation, and operational conditions) and on

the electric parameters of the earth (specific resistance of the layers of soil directly under rails, presence of paths of good conductivity in the ground: sewage, water-bearing pressures, metallic conductors).

The currents leaking from the rails of traction network on the surface may be carried underground through conductive layers of the rock and metallic objects incorporated in the shafts which extend from the surface down to the underground sections. Between the surface and the underground levels of mines there is an non-uniform rock, whose lower strata are, as a rule, characterized by a higher specific resistance than the soil horizons at the surface. In addition, shunting of resistance of the deeper rock strata may occur due to the presence of underground water with high conductivity. Therefore, the presence of metallic devices in shafts, such as:

— pipes for stowing, dewatering, fire fighting, compressed air, and methane venting,
— power and communications cables sheaths and armouring as well as other elements of protective cable earthering systems,
— other devices as, e.g. wood chutes and winding equipment,

is of substantial importance for evaluating the possibility of conducting stray currents to underground working.

Since these pipelines and cables branch underground into various workings and preparatory headings, favourable conditions exist for stray currents to be propagated over substantial areas of the mine working.

The possibility of stray current cumulating in conductive shaft components and being transmitted into underground working is primarily influenced by two factors:

— the location of shafts close to electrified lines (railways), within the zone of influence of electric current fields; in this situation a position of the stray currents induced in the ground may penetrate metallic devices in contact with the ground (rock),
— the means and extent of electrical connections between shaft components and traction rails; the presence of metallic elements between the shaft and the underground and surface rails, the way in which the metallic components are incorporated into the shaft and the degree of water saturation in the vicinity of the top of the shaft are decisive in this respect.

A particularly favourable situation, which furthers the transmission of stray currents from the surface into the underground sections of a mine occurs when electrified lines (of sand used for stoway) railway sidings are led directly into the mine area [18].

In many cases electrified railway lines and tram lines (in the case of mines located in the centre of urban areas), may also be of great importance.

The operation of electric contact traction networks on the surface may be of considerable importance as far as the intensity of stray currents is concerned, particularly in the workings of mines, which do not use electric traction underground. However, even in fully electrified mines, the possibility of the transmission of stray currents from the surface should be taken into account, e.g. when the power supply to underground traction has been switched off in order to avoid possible hazards during blasting.

The above considerations also apply when analysing the effect of the transmission of stray currents induced by the operation of cable traction on levels of a mine other than the one being investigated.

In particular, real conditions, other devices and phenomena, which could act as sources of stray currents, shall be considered.

In an open-cast mine, for example, the currents induced by high-frequency (e.g. radio frequency) electromagnetic fields can be dangerous, whereas in the underground sections of a mine we are more concerned with stray currents, whose "source" is constituted by the circuits of communication, control and warning systems.

In practice, stray currents induced by various factors may complement each other (add up); e.g. in the underground sections of methane-rich mines, the relatively low values of the local currents of electrolytic cells may be increased by currents transferred from the surface in the external circuit.

Finally, we have to state that the intensity, nature and time of occurrence of stray currents in mines depends on many different factors. In many cases, random factors influence the stray currents, as they do most of the events in mines, and in order to evaluate these objectively, the methods of analysis of stochastic processes should also be used [18].

Measurements carried out in mines showed that stray currents taking the form of short-lasting (shorter than one second) impulses are also present.

The most important reason for the occurrence of pulse stray currents is constituted by rapid changes in the load current of the electric traction rails caused by the following transient situations:

— a train starting to move from a full stop and the jerks caused by the slackness of the coupling, as well as its driving through switches or crossings and the temporarily derailment (loss of contact between wheels and track) of a part of the train,

— "whipping" of the current collector (pantograph) against the contact wire or of the wheels against the rails,

— sparking caused by a dynamic change in the contact of the rail with the roadbed (the ground or earthed metallic objects) along the route,

— overvoltages, arc-shortings, and the switching on and off of feeders using quick circuit breakers.

The final nature and peak value as well as the time course of a stray current pulse is also influenced by the parameters of the internal and external circuit. Pulse currents, similar to direct and alternating stray currents, propagate long distances from their point of origin. Research results (oscillographic measurements) confirm that pulse currents reach values, which can be dangerous for electric detonators, namely 0.2–1.1 A between the rock and the rails and 0.08–0.2 A between the rails and pipelines, which together with pulse durations of 1 to 10 ms represent a thermal pulse of 0.01 to 24 $A^2 \cdot ms$. Pulse currents with duration times greater than 100 ms have also been found.

4.2 Rectifier stations as sources of electromagnetic interference

To supply the contact systems in underground mine tunnels, it is a common practice to use mobile automatic rectifier stations of the type APSPa, and sometimes APSPb (Fig. 4.1).

The commutative processes in the six-pulse rectifier of these stations constitute the source of interference voltages which have a line spectrum in which the $6n$ harmonics (with a 300 Hz multiple) predominate.

Expanding the function of the output voltage u (with maximum a value U_m) of a station in the "no-load" state into a Fourier series and taking into account the symmetry of the time function relative to axis of ordinates, we can write (for a mains with frequency 50 Hz)

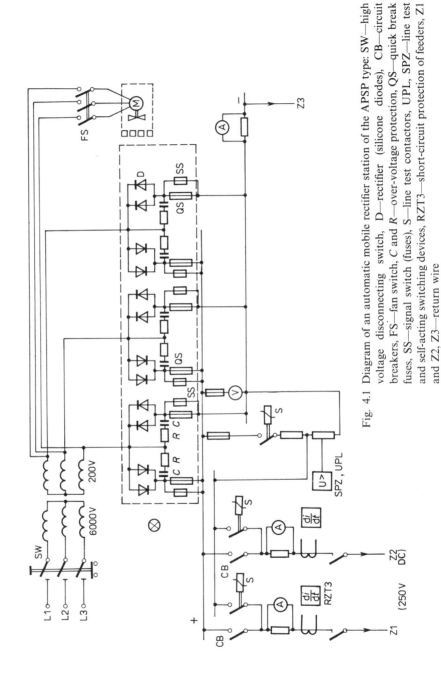

Fig. 4.1 Diagram of an automatic mobile rectifier station of the APSP type: SW—high voltage disconnecting switch, D—rectifier (silicone diodes), CB—circuit breakers, FS—fan switch, C and R—over-voltage protection, QS—quick break fuses, SS—signal switch (fuses), S—line test contactors, UPL, SPZ—line test and self-acting switching devices, RZT3—short-circuit protection of feeders, Z1 and Z2, Z3—return wire

$$u = \frac{3U_m}{\pi} + \sum_{n=1}^{\infty} \frac{3U_m}{\pi} \frac{2(-1)^{n-1}}{(6n-1)(6n+1)} \cos 6n(314t). \tag{4.1}$$

The values calculated from formula (4.1), e.g. of the seven subsequent harmonics in the output voltage of an unloaded station, are given in Table 4.1 and in Fig. 4.2. The table gives also the range of values of these voltages (contact wire—rails) as measured in several mines. The difference in these values is primarily due to the fact that in the real

TABLE 4.1   Calculated and measured values of voltage harmonics (contact wire — rails)

f [Hz]	U_f [V]	
	Calculated	Measured
300	10.4	7–10.6
600	7.5	2–5
900	1.1	1–2
1200	0.6	0.6–1
1500	0.4	0.4–1
1800	0.4	0.3–1
2100	0.3	0.1–0.8

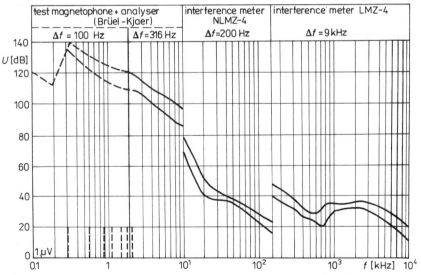

Fig. 4.2 Range of variations of the peak values of interference voltages generated by an unloaded rectifier station of the APSPa type ($\Delta f \triangleq B_i$)

conditions the stations being examined were partly loaded (heading illumination, semaphores), and the measurements were carried out in the network at various distances from the station. Measurements carried out under laboratory conditions agreed closely with the calculated values.

At the higher frequencies, the spectrum of interference is continuous and decreases as the frequency increases. The results of such measurements are given in Fig. 4.2. The measurements were carried out using a peak value detector, and only the maximum, randomly changing indications of interference meters were read; in the figure an area is indicated which represents the maximum values obtained from numerous measurements in several mines. The discontinuities represent the effect of the use of meters with various pulse band widths B_i. It should be mentioned that for frequencies of up to a few kHz the interference voltage has a line spectrum (Table 4.1). For the sake of better legibility, their range has been illustrated by a broken line, as a continuous spectrum, in Fig. 4.2. For frequencies above 10 kHz, the measurements were carried out at certain points only for the frequencies recommended in Polish standards [67], whereas in Fig. 4.2, the characteristic is conventionally drawn with a continuous line.

For the sake of comparison, it should be mentioned that the feeding system for electric traction presently used by the Polish Railways uses a 3 kV DC voltage obtained from mercury rectifiers or from semiconductor rectifiers. From the point of view of protecting the surrounding against electromagnetic interference, these supply stations were examined by measuring the intensity of the interference field within the band of 0.15–30 MHz at a distance of 10 m from the boundary of the "isolated area" which is constituted by the area of a supply station. In this frequency range, the magnetic component of field intensity was primarily measured, in special cases, depending on circumstances, the electric component was also measured. Investigations carried out for the Polish Railways [21, 22] prove that the radioelectric interference emitted by supply stations was, on average, some 15 dB lower than the level of the interference field intensity permitted by Polish standards for suburban traction. Comparing the results of investigations, we used the stricter requirements of standards formulated for suburban and city transport, and not those formulated for long-distance transport; in this case the permissible level determined by the standard is represented by a straight line between the parameters 60 dB for 0.15 MHz and 40 dB for 30 MHz (the level of 0 dB corresponds to the interference field intensity $K_0 = 1$ μV/m).

Radioelectric interference produced in the rectifier assemblies of the supply stations may also penetrate through the traction network into the railway track. The asymmetric component of the interference voltage, which originates in supply substations flows along the wires of the contact system and along the earth, its loop may be of considerable size and possesses good radiation properties.

Widespread interference in a traction network may also be caused by switching off the assembly of tuned filters in a rectifier traction station, e.g. as a result of a blown fuse. Then, a rectified current with highly variable components, flows into the contact system. The most influential components are those with the frequencies of 150, 300, 600, 900, ... Hz. These produce interference in the operation of overhead communication lines spread along the railway tracks; interference in the operation of railway traffic protection systems may also occur.

4.3   Electric locomotives as sources of interference

An electric locomotive (Fig. 4.3) consists of many systems, which can generate electromagnetic interference with various frequencies and of varying intensity. Of particular importance are sparking at contacts (pantograph, wheels) and the commutation processes of internal systems (motors, thyristor and contact switches, starting and adjustment devices). The level of interference produced by the contact of the pantograph with the contact wire depends on the type and condition of the pantograph, the locomotive speed and the condition and structure of the contact system. The source of interference is, in this case, a "spark-gap generator" of variable power and generally low impedance. Sparking of pantograph occurs when the contact between it and the contact wire is broken; this happens most often when passing through switches, boundaries of supply zones of rectifier stations and section switches. When the locomotive is moving the break of contact between the collector and the wire may be either total or partial. In both cases, a high frequency electric oscillation is generated. Sparking of a collector at a given point is a transient but repetitive phenomenon. At the same time one should remember that the power of a spark or electric arc is

contact wire

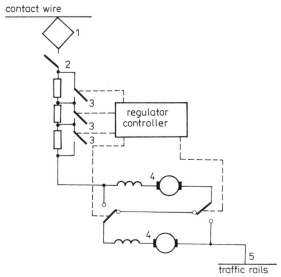

Fig. 4.3 Simplified schematic diagram of an underground electric locomotive of the Ld
type with the "sources" of interferences marked: 1—pantograph, 2—quick circuit
breaker, 3—regulation resistors switches, 4—motor with series characteristic,
5—wheel–rails contact

relatively high and that a contact wire, insulated from earth, functions as
a transmitting antenna.

The phenomena of sparking at the contact between the wheels and the
rails are of a similar nature and can be particularly intense if the track
and the interrail connections are in bad condition. The interference
generated by commutator motors result from the commutation of the
current and is substantially influenced by the condition of the commutator and brushes (e.g. commutator contamination, use of improper
brushes, mechanical damage to commutator or brush-holders). As these
machines operate for lengthy periods during each cycle of locomotive
operation, sparking under brushes must be treated as a serious source of
interference.

Arc processes, which occur in switches (quick switches, contactors,
fuses, etc.), occasionally cause brief pulses of rapidly declining electromagnetic waves with a broad frequency band. The internal components of a locomotive are located in metallic (steel) casings which
function as screens for both emitted and received electromagnetic

interference pulses. Isolating the main sources of interference is very difficult in practice since a traction vehicle emits interference during driving, when individual devices which constitute the sources of interference operate simultaneously and are functionally interdependent. We can only mention that in the analysis of the results of investigations of electric locomotives of the Polish Railways [21, 22] it was found that the pantograph constitutes the most important source of interference emitted. Confirmation of this research is provided by measurements carried out on electric mine locomotives; these results are presented in Fig. 4.4 [30]. Curve 2 in Fig. 4.4 was obtained for the operation of an electric locomotive which was directly connected to the rectifier station (laboratory measurements); curves 1 and 3 represent the results of measurements in a mine, during normal operation of locomotives (operation with a pantograph). Interference voltages were measured by placing a probe, with interference meter attached to it, directly onto the contact (trolley) wire. For each frequency measured

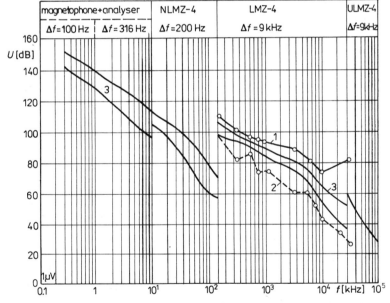

Fig. 4.4 Range of variations of the values of interference voltages U in individual frequency bands $\Delta f(B_i)$ in a contact wire during the operation of electric locomotives: 1, 3—locomotive drive, 2—motionless locomotive operation, (1—thyristor locomotive)

(selected according to the Polish standard [67]), a locomotive performed one operational cycle consisting of: starting the locomotive close to the measurement point, a smooth drive, breaking at a distance of about 50 m and return to the starting point (Fig. 4.5a). Interference measure-

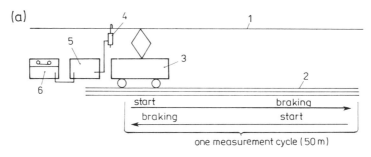

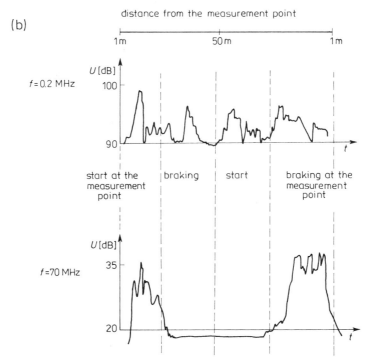

Fig. 4.5 Example of interference voltage measurements in a contact wire for two cycles of electric locomotive operation (forward and return): 1—contact wire, 2—rails, 3—locomotive, 4—test probe, 5—interference meter, 6—converter and magneto-phone

ments were made while the locomotive was driven with both low and high current consumption. Figure 4.5 presents the layout of the measuring system and examples of record of the variation of interference with time for two frequencies (carried out for one drive cycle).

In the lower frequency range (up to 10 kHz) the interference voltages were registered with an instrumentation tape recorder, and they were then subjected to spectral analysis using Brüel–Kjaer equipment. The analysis of these results allows us to state that the differences between the maximum levels of interference voltages measured in several mines do not exceed twenty decibels; they reflect the variable condition of the rolling stock and different types of electric locomotives investigated. The spectrum of interference voltages within the range of up to a few kHz is a line spectrum with frequencies being multiples of 300 Hz. For higher frequencies the interference spectrum is continuous.

On the basis of the results of the measurements carried out so far we can state that the maximum levels of interference voltages occur during the course of starting and braking an electric locomotive. The highest values of interference voltages, within the entire frequency range, are generated by electric locomotives with a thyristor starter (chopper). This can be seen for example in Fig. 4.4, where curve 1 denotes the maximum levels of interference voltages, which occur in a contact wire during the operation of a thyristor-equipped locomotive. Curves 2 and 3 show results for locomotives with resistance starters.

TABLE 4.2   Example of the results of calculations and measurements of the content of harmonics in rectifier station (APSPa) output voltage loaded with the current I_0

f [Hz]	$I_0 = 0$		$I_0 = 260A$		$I_0 = 350A$	
	U_f [V]	$U_\% = \dfrac{U_f}{\Sigma U_f} 100\%$	U_f [V]	$U_\%$ [%]	U [V]	$U_\%$ [%]
100	0.4	3.0	0.5	3.5	0.25	1.7
300	10.4	83.3	12.5	84.5	12.5	81.7
600	2.6	21.7	3.1	21.6	3.1	20.8
900	1.2	9.5	2.2	15.2	2.9	19.2
1200	0.7	6.2	2.1	14.7	2.3	15.5
1500	0.4	3.3	1.5	10.5	1.5	10.0
ΣU_f	12	100	14.5	100	15	100

For a thyristor-equipped locomotive, more detailed laboratory investigations and spectral analysis of the output voltages and current (in the contact wire) as well as the voltage and current feeding a rectifier station (6 kV), were carried out. Measurements of the output current were made using a current detector, connected to a 300 A shunt, with an instrumentation tape recorder and spectrum analyser. The alternating current and voltage on the 6 kV side were measured using current and voltage transformers with an instrumentation tape recorder. The measurements covered the range of acoustic frequencies up to 10 kHz. Selected results of measurements of the harmonic content in the rectifier output voltage, for different values of locomotive load currents I_0 are given in Table 4.2, while Fig. 4.6 shows an example of data records (as a function of time) for two harmonics.

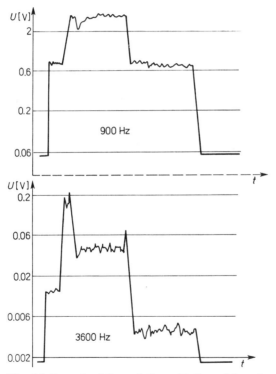

Fig. 4.6 Example of the variation with time of the values of two harmonics in the input voltage of a rectifier station of the APSPa type loaded with a thyristor locomotive $(I_0 = 350 \text{ A})$

An analysis of the variation time of voltage harmonics shows that up to a frequency of about 1.5 kHz, they depend only slightly on the mode of operation of the locomotive (starting, steady operation). At higher frequencies, substantial differences occur between the voltages during starting and smooth driving (Fig. 4.7). The maximum values of output voltage recorded in the laboratory are in general agreement with those measured in mines (Fig. 4.4). In a 6 kV network feeding an APSPa mobile rectifier station, no higher harmonics which could be directly connected

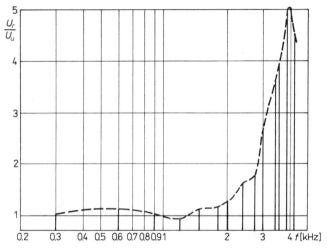

Fig. 4.7 Influence of starting a thyristor locomotive on the value of harmonics in the output voltage of a rectifier station of the APSPa type; U_r—voltage during starting, U_u—voltage during stable drive ($I_0 = 350$ A)

with the operation of an electric locomotive (high shorting power in the 6 kV network) were found. An analysis of the results of the harmonics of the output current and the current (6 kV) feeding the APSPa rectifier station, are presented in Figs. 4.8 and 4.9. In the station output current, the same harmonics, i.e. the sixth, twelfth, eighteenth, etc. (300 Hz, 600 Hz, 900 Hz, ...), which occur in the output voltage, were observed; as for the voltages, a substantial dependence on the operation conditions and the load of a locomotive can be seen. Characteristic harmonics also appear in the current feeding the rectifier station on the 6 kV side. The even harmonics $6n$ (300, 600, 900 Hz) do not occur there, instead we observe the uneven harmonics of the order $6n-1$ or $6n+1$, i.e. 5, 7, 11,

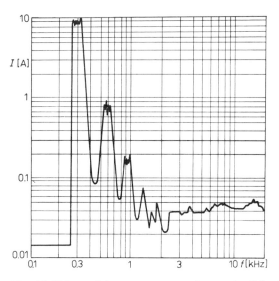

Fig. 4.8 Values of the output current harmonics I (in the contact wire) of an APSPa rectifier station loaded with the current $I_0 = 260$ A consumed by a thyristor locomotive

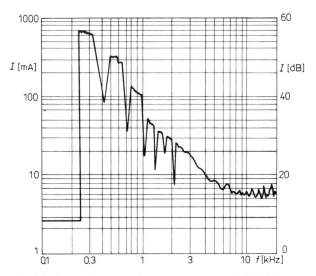

Fig. 4.9 Values of current harmonics I on the 6 kV side of an APSPa rectifier station (when loaded with an electric locomotive, $I_0 = 260$ A)

13, 17, 19, etc. The values of these current harmonics are practically
independent of the operation mode of the locomotive (starting, smooth
driving). This can be seen from the analyses of the time plots of individual
harmonics which are presented in Table 4.3.

Results of measurements of pulse interference in electric traction
networks, carried out in USSR mines [41], are presented in Fig. 4.10.
Comparing them with the results presented in Fig. 4.4, we can notice the

TABLE 4.3   Content of higher harmonics I_f in the 6 kV
input current of an APSPa rectifier station ($I_0 = 260A$)

f [Hz]	I_f [A]	$\dfrac{I_f}{\Sigma I_f} \cdot 100$ [%]
50	6.4	95.7
250	1.17	17.4
300	—	—
350	0.72	10.7
550	0.41	9.1
600	—	—
650	0.28	4.4
850	0.16	2.4
900	—	—
950	0.12	1.7
1150	0.07	1.0
1200	—	—
1250	0.06	0.8
ΣI_f	6.7	100

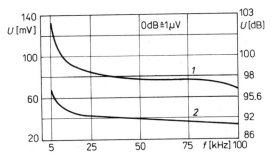

Fig. 4.10 Values of interferences U in a contact wire: 1—mean values, 2—standard
deviation

correspondence of the maximum levels of interference voltages within the range up to 50 kHz.

Measurements of the radio noise emitted by rolling stock of surface traction are carried out using interference meters equipped with measuring antennas.

These investigations can be carried out using either a stationary method or a wagon method, i.e. from a moving measuring point.

The stationary method consists in placing an assembly of measuring antennas of the interference meter at a distance of 10 m horizontally from the nearest wire of the contact system, at a height of 1 m above the ground (for the frequency range of 0.15 to 30 MHz), or at a height of 3 m (for the range of 30 to 300 MHz).

Before beginning the measurements, it is necessary to check at each measuring frequency for any outside interference or emission of transmitting stations. The level of outside interference must be lower by at least 10 dB than the interference produced by the object being investigated.

The locomotive being investigated moves along the length of a railway track isolated in this way and closed to both passenger and freight traffic. The measurements are carried out at each frequency for both low and high currents, with the pantograph up and down, during starting and braking of the locomotive. During the taking of the measurements, the entire auxiliary electric equipment of the locomotive (fans, compressors, buzzers, etc.) should be operating.

Measurements by the moving point method are conducted from a laboratory rail-coach with measurement antennas installed on it. Such a rail-coach is coupled to the locomotive being investigated. This method makes it possible to prolong the time of observation and to measure the interference for the selected frequencies while in motion, as well as (in co-operation with a steam locomotive) measuring the interference emitted by the contact system. The disadvantage of this method is the necessity of converting the results into values, compatible with those measured using the stationary method.

The results of the measurements show that the level of interference emitted by a locomotive with its pantograph down is much lower than the interference levels produced with the pantograph up. The level of the interference emitted most often was below the sensitivity of the equipment.

Measurements on diesel-electric locomotives (types ST-44, SP-54) reveal a level of emitted interference lower by some 20 dB on average than specified in the standard and also lower than the level of interference emitted by electric locomotives.

On the basis of this research it is not possible to demonstrate a clear interdependence between the interference emitted and the current input from the contact system, nor any influence of such factors as starting and braking.

The results of the measurements show that the mean level of radio noise emitted by electric locomotives drops with an increase in frequency from about 50–55 dB at 150 kHz to about 30 dB at 30 MHz. For the higher frequencies (up to 300 MHz) the interference field strength, is contained within the limits 30–40 dB.

The mean level of interference at a given frequency and a vehicle of a given type has been calculated on the basis of the results of 10 tests including:
— 3 drives with high current consumption,
— 3 drives with low current consumption,
— 2 drives of a starting type,
— 2 drives with breaking the vehicle.

The standard deviation in the range of 0.15–30 MHz for the EU-07 electric locomotive and for the EN-57 electric unit is, on average, 4.5 dB, and in the range of 30–300 MHz, about 3 dB. The distribution of the mean levels of interference in the sample for each frequency is normal.

4.4 Transmission of interference by contact lines

Contact lines should be regarded as asymmetrical transmission lines, which carry the interference produced by rectifier stations and electric locomotives for considerable distances. The parameters of a contact system are the predominant influence on electromagnetic wave propagation along the contact wires and the propagation of interference in mine workings. Statistical investigations carried out in the former USSR [38] reveal that the values of the basic parameters of a mining contact (trolley) system (at the 95% confidence level) are contained within the following limits:

resistance 0.814–0.936 $\Omega \cdot km^{-1}$,
inductivity 1.496–1.594 $mH \cdot km^{-1}$,

leakage   0.037–0.053 mS·km^{-1},
capacity   0.049–0.063 μF·km^{-1}.

The characteristic impedance of mine traction lines may be determined with accuracy [12] sufficient for practical needs, from the
following, approximate, formula:

$$Z_{ch} = 48 \sqrt{\ln \frac{R}{r} \ln \frac{2h}{r}} , \qquad (4.2)$$

where

 R — radius of heading (tunnel),
 h — distance between the contact wire and the side wall,
 r — radius of the contact wire.

 Figure 4.11 illustrates the relationship between the characteristic
impedance Z_{ch} of the contact system and the frequency for the range 30
to 139 kHz [12]; it can be seen that the frequency exerts only a very
minor influence on the value of impedance. We can assume that, on
average, the value of the characteristic impedance is 260 Ω for system in
a single-track heading (curves 1 in Fig. 4.11) and 120 Ω—for the system in
a double-track heading (curves 2). The influence of the presence of a great
number of long conductors (cables, pipelines) in a heading is represented

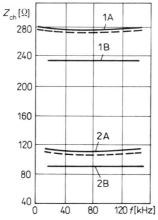

Fig. 4.11 Plot of the characteristic impedance Z_{ch} of a traction network in function of the
   frequency f, considering the influence of the number of tracks (1, 2), presence of
   long conductors (A, B) and rock mass conductivity (continuous and broken
   lines)

by curves B in Fig. 4.11. In practice, the electrical conductivity γ of the rock mass surrounding the heading influences the characteristic impedance to a minor extent; in Fig. 4.11, this influence is represented by the difference in the values of Z_{ch} for $\gamma_1 = 10^{-3}$ S·m^{-1} (continuous curve) and for $\gamma_2 = 10^{-1}$ S·m^{-1} (broken curve).

Figure 4.12 shows the influence of the frequency f upon the attenuation of a contact system in single-track heading (curve 1), and in

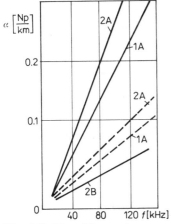

Fig. 4.12 Plot of the traction network attenuation constant α in function of the frequency f, considering the influence of the number of tracks (1, 2), presence of long conductors (A, B) and rock mass conductivity (continuous and broken lines)

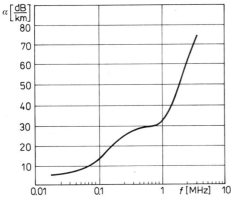

Fig. 4.13 Influence of frequency f upon the attenuation constant α of an underground traction line

double-track heading (curve 2), and also demonstrate the influence of the
presence of metallic masses (curve B) and that of the conductivity of the
surrounding rock mass (continuous curves γ_1 and broken curves γ_2)
[12]. The influence of the higher frequencies on the attenuation of the
contact system (all the receivers and rectifier station disconnected) is
presented in Fig. 4.13 [30]. The substantial increase in the attenuation
factor with increasing frequency is mostly the result of the skin effect.

4.5   The storage-battery locomotive as a source of radio noise

The storage-battery locomotives presently used in mines contain
a chopper, and do therefore constitute a source of interference. Figure
4.14 presents a block diagram of the Lea BM-12/3T locomotive, with
particular stress placed on the elements causing electromagnetic interference. The locomotive is supplied from a 144 V storage battery.
Regulation of the motor supply voltage is carried out by the chopper,
which contains a main thyristor MT and a commutative thyristor CT.
Both thyristors are controlled by a series of gate pulses with a frequency

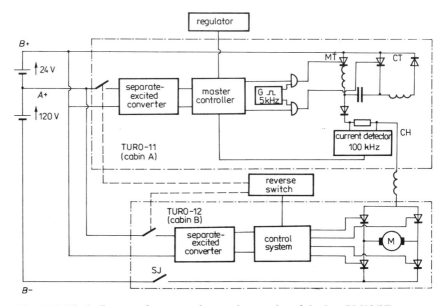

Fig. 4.14 Block diagram of a storage-battery locomotive of the Lea BM12/3T type

of about 5 kHz. A chopper master controller regulates the switching on the MT and CT thyristors, using two-state current regulation. The current in the main circuit of the locomotive is measured by sensor with conversion at a frequency of about 100 kHz. The strength of the current in the main circuit of the locomotive is compared with the strength of the current from the controller. Based on this comparison gate pulses are sent to either the CT or the MT thyristor. The electronic systems of the locomotive are contained in two flame-proof boxes (TURO 11 and TURO 12) both located in the locomotive cabin. The electronic systems are supplied with 24 V taken from an additional branch of the storage-battery set. Appropriate supply voltages for the electronic systems are produced in two separately excited converters, operating at a frequency of about 5 kHz. The following interference sources can be identified in the locomotive (Fig. 4.14): the DC commutator motor M, the chopper CH, the gate pulse generator G, the current detector and the independently activated converters.

Measurements show [31] that the independently activated converters which generate interference with a line spectrum, and the chopper which generates pulse-type interference, are the predominant (sources) of interference. Figure 4.15 presents the spectrum of the magnetic component of the interference field measured at a distance of 1 m from the

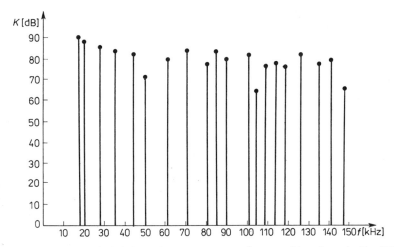

Fig. 4.15 Magnetic field intensity spectrum at a distance of 1 m from the Lea BM12/3T
         locomotive

side of the locomotive. The magnetic component of the field is first of all
induced by the current flow in the cables A +, B + (Fig. 4.14) feeding the
independently activated converters (in the TURO 11 and TURO 12
boxes). The current spectrum in cables A + and B + is presented in Fig.
4.16. Currents flowing in the remaining cables of the locomotive are
lower than those in cables A + and B +.

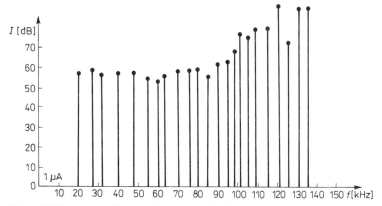

Fig. 4.16 Spectrum of current harmonics in the A +, B + cables of the Lea BM12/3T
locomotive

Examples of current values in different cables, measured with the
NLMZ-4 type meter with a pulse bandwidth of 9 kHz and tuned to
a frequency of 100 kHz, are as follows:
  — A + and B + cables   87 dB,
  — B — cable   57 dB,
  — cables to lamps   39 dB.
Switching the chopper on does not change the mean current value in
the B + cable (as measured with an average detector) but the quasi-peak
value increases.

4.6   The electric field of a contact wire in a heading

The main quantity, which characterizes an electromagnetic field is the
vector of the electric field intensity **K**. From the fourth Maxwell equation
(2.6) it follows that an electric field, variable in time, constitutes the

source of a magnetic field. In the general case, the field vector $\mathbf{K}$ is made up of two components—static component: $\mathbf{K}_s$ and an induced one: $\mathbf{K}_i$, i.e.

$$\mathbf{K} = \mathbf{K}_s + \mathbf{K}_i. \tag{4.3}$$

In a space with conductivity γ and magnetic permeability μ, and for a current with angular frequency ω, we have [15, 16]:

$$\mathbf{K}_s = -\frac{1}{\mu\gamma}\,\text{curl div}\,\mathbf{A} = -\text{curl}\,V, \tag{4.4}$$

$$\mathbf{K}_i = -j\omega\mathbf{A}, \tag{4.5}$$

where V is the scalar potential, whereas $\mathbf{A}$ is the vector potential of an electromagnetic field.

The vector potential $\mathbf{A}$ at a distance r from a conductor of infinitely small section and length dl with a current I, drawn along the curve L, is given by the relationship [16]:

$$\mathbf{A} = \mu I \int\limits_{L} \frac{e^{-kr}}{4\pi r}\,dl, \tag{4.6}$$

where

$$k^2 = j\omega\mu\gamma. \tag{4.7}$$

In workings, whose length is many times longer than their transverse dimensions, the electric field needs to be analysed only in one plane, perpendicular to the axis of the heading. The shape of the cross-section of such a heading containing a contact system depends on the type of lining used. The type of lining used most often is that of an arched support consisting of three arches (roof arch and two side wall arches) and a straight floor (foot-wall). For purposes of analysis we can approximate the shape of the heading by a semi-circle of radius R (Fig. 4.19).

The distribution of a planar electric field may be obtained using conformal mapping [10, 11]. The function

$$w = \frac{1}{2}\left(z - \frac{1}{z}\right) \tag{4.8}$$

presents the mapping of the upper semi-circle ($|z| < 1$) onto the bottom half-plane ($\text{Im}\,z < 0$). The distribution of a linear charge field over the surface of the ground may be determined using the image-charge method. Thus, function (4.6) may be used for determining the distribution of an electric field in a heading of semi-circular cross-section.

The distribution of the equipotential lines of an electric field originating from a wire suspended above the surface of the ground is presented in Fig. 4.17. After applying the inverse transformation to (4.8)

$$z = w \pm \sqrt{w-1} \qquad (4.9)$$

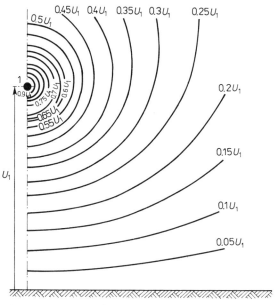

Fig. 4.17 Equipotential lines of a linear charge field (wire 1) over the surface of the ground

we obtain the image of the electric field of a contact wire in a heading, e.g. at the distance $h = 0.9\ R$ from the foot-wall (Fig. 4.18).

Placing another conductor 2 with a radius r_2 in the field produced by conductor 1 of radius r_1, at a distance considerably greater than the transverse dimensions of both conductors (Fig. 4.19), will not cause any change in the distribution of charges on the surface of conductor 1 and in the contour of the heading. This permits us to use equation (4.8) to calculate the capacity between the two conductors in the heading.

Assuming the location of the two conductors suspended in a heading to be as shown in Fig. 4.19a then, after using transformation (4.8) we obtain a new distribution (Fig. 4.19b). Partial capacities in a system such as that in Fig. 4.19b may be calculated from the following formulas [15]:

$$C_{12} = \frac{\varphi_{12}}{\varphi_{11}\varphi_{22} - \varphi_{12}^2},$$ (4.10)

$$C_{10} = \frac{\varphi_{22} - \varphi_{12}}{\varphi_{11}\varphi_{22} - \varphi_{12}^2},$$ (4.11)

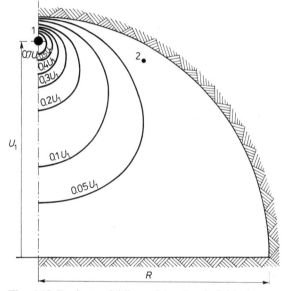

Fig. 4.18 Equipotential lines of the electric field of a contact wire 1 in a dog heading of radius R

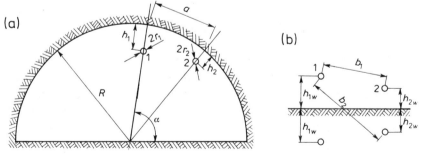

Fig. 4.19 Sketch illustrating the distribution of the cables 1, 2: (a) in a heading with the radius R and (b) its conformal mapping

$$C_{20} = \frac{\varphi_{11} - \varphi_{12}}{\varphi_{11}\varphi_{22} - \varphi_{12}^2},$$

(4.12)

where

$$\varphi_{11} = \frac{1}{2\pi\varepsilon_0} \ln \frac{2h_{1w}}{r},$$

(4.13)

$$\varphi_{22} = \frac{1}{2\pi\varepsilon_0} \ln \frac{2h_{2w}}{r_2},$$

(4.14)

$$\varphi_{12} = \frac{1}{2\pi\varepsilon_0} \ln \frac{b_1}{b_2}.$$

(4.15)

Examples of capacity values for wires of 1 m length calculated from these formulas are presented in Table 4.4; for these calculations values of $\alpha = 90°$, $h_1 = 0.4$ m, $h_2 = 0.2$ m, and $R = 2$ m were assumed.

TABLE 4.4   Values of partial capacities calculated for the system presented in Fig. 4.19a

a [m]	0.5	1	2	0.5	1	2	0.5	1	2
r_1 [mm]	1	1	1	10	10	10	10	10	10
r_2 [mm]	1	1	1	1	1	1	10	10	10
c_{12} [pF/m]	0.5	0.19	0.07	0.77	0.28	0.1	1.26	0.47	0.16
c_{10} [pF/m]	7.7	8	8.1	11.6	12	12.2	11.2	11.8	12.2
c_{20} [pF/m]	8.7	9.1	9.2	8.5	9	9.2	14	14.6	14.9

4.7   Examples of the electric interaction of a contact line

The electric interaction of a contact (trolley) wire (1) upon a symmetrical wire track (2) loaded asymmetrically can be presented schematically as the system shown in Fig. 4.20. To qualitatively illustrate the interaction under consideration, the following values of the system and circuit parameters have been adopted:

$$C_{12} = 0.5 \frac{pF}{m}; \quad C_{20} = 10 \frac{pF}{m} \text{ (Table 4.4);}$$

$$C_{23} = 7\frac{pF}{m}\;(YTKGMFLY\;1\times2\times0.5\;mm^2);\; l = 1000\;m;$$

$$Z_a = Z_b = 600\;\Omega,\; X_{C12} = \frac{1}{\omega C_{12}l} = 314\;k\Omega,$$

$$X_{C2} = \frac{1}{\omega(C_{23}+C_{20})l} = 1.88\;k\Omega.$$

The calculated values of the capacitive reactance show that in the substitute diagram (Fig. 4.20b) we can for the sake of simplicity, disregard the parallel reactance X_{C2} (of the capacitance of the object experiencing interference). Then, the voltage U_{23} (voltage drop across the Z_a impedance) in the circuit experiencing interference is expressed as follows (Fig. 4.20):

$$U_{23} = jU_1\omega C_{12}l\frac{Z_aZ_b}{Z_a+Z_b}. \tag{4.16}$$

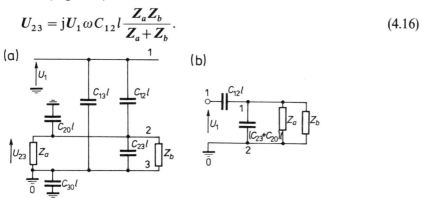

Fig. 4.20 Substitute diagrams of the electric interaction between a contact wire and a symmetrical circuit loaded asymmetrically: (a) complete and (b) simplified

If we assume the following spectrum of interference voltages in the contact wire [30]:

$$f = 300\;Hz,\quad U_1 = 12\;V,$$

$$f = 600\;Hz,\quad U_1 = 6\;V,$$

$$f = 900\;Hz,\quad U_1 = 2\;V,$$

$$f = 1200\;Hz,\quad U_1 = 2\;V$$

and performing the calculations according to formula (4.16), we obtain the following values for the voltage drop across the impedance Z_a: $U_{23} = 3.39$ mV for $f = 300$ Hz, $U_{23} = 1.69$ mV for $f = 600$ Hz, $U_{23} = 1.69$ mV for $f = 900$ Hz, $U_{23} = 2.26$ mV for $f = 1200$ Hz.

In the above example of electric interaction a schematic circuit with lumped parameters (Fig. 4.20) was used. For a more accurate analysis, a substitute diagram with distributed parameters should be used. Then, in every elementary (infinitesimal section) of length dx the current

$$I_{12}dx = jU_1\omega C_{12}dx \tag{4.17}$$

should be considered, which results from the interaction of the contact wire 1 with the elementary length of the communication line 2 (Fig. 4.21).

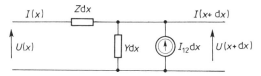

Fig. 4.21 Substitute diagram of the capacitive interaction upon an infinitestimal section of a telecommunication circuit

The method of analysis of a circuit (line) with distributed parameters (Fig. 4.21) is given in [36]. Here, U_{23} at the input terminals of the lines was determined from the following equations:

$$U_{23} = \frac{I_{12}(x)}{Y} \frac{Z_a[Z_w(1-\cosh\Gamma l) - Z_b\sinh\Gamma l]}{(Z_w^2 + Z_a Z_b)\sinh\Gamma l + Z_w(Z_a + Z_b)\cosh\Gamma l}, \tag{4.18}$$

where

$$Z_w = \sqrt{\frac{Z}{Y}}$$ —characteristic wave impedance of the line,

$$\Gamma = \sqrt{ZY}$$ —propagation coefficient.

From these formulas, ordering the same circuit parameters as before, the following U_{23} values were calculated: 3.17 mV for 300 Hz, 1.58 mV for 600 Hz, 1.57 mV for 900 Hz, 2.07 mV for 1200 Hz. Comparing the two sets of values obtained shows that the error introduced by using the model with lumped parameter did not exceed 10%. This is accurate enough from most practical purposes.

In the case of a symmetrical overhead circuit which is symmetrically loaded, the asymmetry of the capacitive coupling of the communications circuit wires relative to contact wire ($C_{12} \neq C_{13}$, Fig. 4.20) causes a so-called *direct interaction*. A substitute diagram of such a system is presented in Fig. 4.22. Assuming that the impedance resulting from the parallel connection of circuits loads Z_a and Z_b is substantially lower than the capacitive reactance between the cores 2 and 3, i.e.

$$\left|\frac{Z_a Z_b}{Z_a + Z_b}\right| \ll \frac{1}{\omega\left(C_{23} + \dfrac{C_{20} C_{30}}{C_{20} + C_{30}}\right)l} \qquad (4.19)$$

we obtain the following relationship between the voltages U_1 and U_{23}:

$$U_{23} = jU_1 \omega c \frac{Z_a Z_b}{Z_a + Z_b}, \qquad (4.20)$$

where

$$c = 0.25(C_{12} - C_{13} + C_{30} - C_{20}). \qquad (4.21)$$

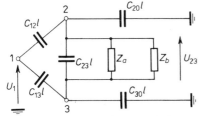

Fig. 4.22 Substitute diagram of the capacitive interaction upon a symmetrical circuit loaded symmetrically

If conductors 2 and 3 of the wire circuit are twisted around each other (e.g. the circuit lies in a cable), the asymmetry of the capacity (in the sense of direct interaction) may be neglected. The reason for the appearance of an interference voltage on the load of such a circuit is due to the asymmetry relative to earth [81]. It can be taken into account by introducing the factor of circuit susceptibility to electric interaction λ_e, defined as follows:

$$\lambda_e = \frac{2U_{23}}{U_c}, \qquad (4.22)$$

where U_c is the so-called *capacitive voltage* [81, 82], equal to the mean value of the voltage in both conductors of the circuit relative earth. Its value can be calculated from the formula

$$U_c = U_1 \frac{C_{12} + C_{13}}{C_{12} + C_{13} + C_{20} + C_{30}}. \qquad (4.23)$$

On the basis of (4.22) and (4.23) we obtain formula (4.24), which allows us to calculate the interference voltage U_{23}

$$U_{23} = \frac{1}{2} \lambda_e \frac{C_{12} + C_{13}}{C_{12} + C_{13} + C_{20} + C_{30}} U_1. \tag{4.24}$$

Measurement carried out on the cable lines showed that the factor λ_e assumes values ranging from 0.001 to 0.04 [28]. Equation (4.24) is accurate for those cases where every of the circuit points (the loads Z_a and Z_b) is not earthed. This happens for example in mines when intrinsically safe feeding bridges are used in which no point on the linear side is earthed (IAUL type in Polish mines). In the case of circuit laid in cables with an earthed conductive sheath, (e.g. lead sheath), or with an earthed armouring, there is no electric interaction ($C_{12} = C_{13} = 0$). In mine networks armoured cables are mostly used, however the final lengths of such circuits are often by unarmoured cables (YTKGMFLY), resulting in electric interactions, which interfere with the quality of transmission.

4.8   The mutual impedance of earth return circuits

In practice electric traction lines in mines usually include an earth return circuit, i.e. an electric circuit of which the earth constitute a part. The earth, as an additional conductor with conductivity γ_{er}, may substantially influence the value of the mutual impedance of the circuits (see formula (3.19)). The alternating current I flowing in a certain circuit (1) (e.g. in a traction line) may excite currents in the earth, which will induce electromotive forces in second circuit (2) (e.g. in a communications line)—independent of the currents flowing in circuit 1. The simplest schematic system of earth return circuits is presented in Fig. 4.23. It contains two parallel conductors of infinite length and infinitely small cross-section (see Fig. 3.1) suspended horizontally in the air above the surface of the ground (earth) which is treated as a uniform, anisotropic, semi-infinite medium with electrical conductivity γ_{er} and magnetic permeability μ_0. The mutual impedance Z_{12} per unit length of the two conductors (1 and 2 in Fig. 4.23) in such a system may be calculated from the relationship [16]:

$$Z_{12} = 4\omega \times 10^{-7}\left[Q(h'_1 + h'_2, a') + \right.$$

$$\left. +j\frac{1}{2}\ln\sqrt{\frac{(h_1 + h_2)^2 + a^2}{(h_1 - h_2)^2 + a^2}}\ \right]\quad \left[\frac{\Omega}{m}\right],\qquad (4.25)$$

where

$h'_1 = h_1|k|,\ h'_2 = h_2|k|,\ a' = a|k|,$

$k = \sqrt{j\omega\gamma_{er}\mu_0},$

$Q(h'_1 + h'_2, a')$ — a function tabularized in [16].

After transformation, we obtain the formula for mutual inductance in the following form:

$$M_{12} = \frac{Z_{12}}{j\omega} = -j\frac{\mu_0 l}{\pi}Q(h'_1 + h'_2, a') +$$

$$+\frac{\mu_0}{2\pi}\ln\sqrt{\frac{(h_1 + h_2)^2 + a^2}{(h_1 - h_2)^2 + a^2}}\quad\left[\frac{H}{m}\right].\qquad (4.26)$$

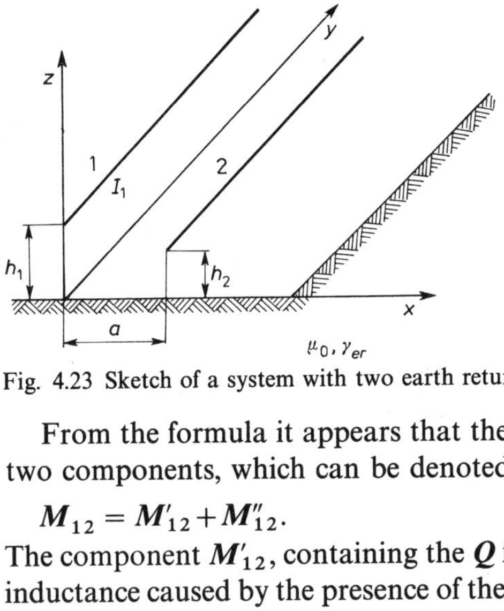

Fig. 4.23 Sketch of a system with two earth return circuits

From the formula it appears that the mutual inductance consists of two components, which can be denoted as M'_{12} and M''_{12}, i.e.

$$M_{12} = M'_{12} + M''_{12}.\qquad (4.27)$$

The component M'_{12}, containing the Q function, represents the mutual inductance caused by the presence of the earth. Owing to the phase shift between the electric field intensity and current density this generally is a complex number. The component M''_{12} stands for the mutual inductance between conductor 1 and the circuit made by conductor 2 and its mirror reflection relative to the surface of the earth (disregarding the earth's conductivity—Fig. 4.24). The value of this component may be calculated as follows [28]:

$$M''_{12} = \frac{\mu_0}{2\pi} \ln \frac{b_2}{b_1},$$ (4.28)

where $b_2 = \sqrt{(h_1 + h_2)^2 + a^2}$, $b_1 = \sqrt{(h_1 - h_2)^2 + a^2}$. In practice, the value M''_{12} may be disregarded as it is very small in comparison to M'_{12}.

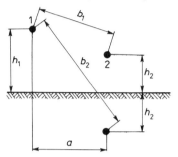

Fig. 4.24 Illustration showing the distances for calculating of mutual inductance M_{12}

If the condition

$$|k|b_1 \leqslant 0.05$$ (4.29)

is met, the function Q may be reduced to the form

$$Q(h'_1 + h'_2, a') = \frac{\pi}{8} + j\frac{1}{2} \ln \frac{1.85}{b'_1},$$ (4.30)

where $b'_1 = b_1|k|$. Then equation (4.26) is reduced to the form

$$M_{12} \approx M'_{12} = -j\frac{\mu_0}{8} + \frac{\mu_0}{2\pi} \ln \frac{1.85}{b'_1}.$$ (4.31)

Figure 4.25 presents the frequency characteristics of the mutual inductance modulus calculated from equation (4.31). The resistivity of most Carboniferous rocks falls within the limits of 2000–27000 $\Omega \cdot$m; the resistivity of Polish hard coals is from 2×10^3 $\Omega \cdot$m, for the Libiąż and Łaziska beds, up to 134×10^3 $\Omega \cdot$m for the Ruda and Wałbrzych beds. Taking into account the fact that large and widely distributed metal objects (pipelines, structures, casing) are commonly present in dog headings and further taking into account water flows and rock moisture, a value of $\gamma_{er} = 0.1$ S·m^{-1} for the earth's conductivity has been assumed in calculations based on formula (4.31) and presented in Fig. 4.25. The broken line in Fig. 4.25 denotes the results of measurements of the resultant of mutual inductance M_{12h} (see Section 4.10) in an experimental drift with a distance of about 1 m between conductors 1 and 2. The value M''_{12}, obtained from the calculations for $h_1 = 0.4$ m and $h_2 = 0.2$ m is equal to 7 nH/m, i.e. it is substantially lower than M'_{12}, which justifies the deletion of M''_{12} relative to M'_{12}.

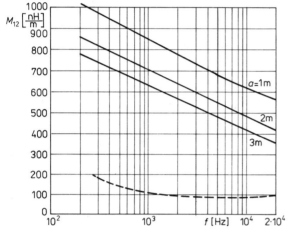

Fig. 4.25 Frequency characteristics of the mutual inductance M_{12} due to earth return circuits 1 and 2 for the case of earth electrical conductivity $\gamma_{er} = 0.1$ S·m^{-1}; broken line marks resultant mutual inductance M_{12h} (see Section 4.10)

In the case of earth return circuits of infinite length (Fig. 4.23), the static component of the electromagnetic field K_{ys}, parallel to the axis, is equal to zero [16]. In the case of conductor 1, having a finite length, the component K_{ys} in the earth is no longer equal to zero, and may substantially influence the value of the mutual inductance of earth return circuits. With the simplifications used, the mutual impedance does not depend on the height of suspension h_1 and h_2 of the wires (see equation (4.31)). Therefore, the consideration can be limited to the situation where both wires 1 and 2 lie on the surface of the ground and the ends of wire 1, which conducts the current I_1, are earthed at the points A_1 and B_1 (Fig. 4.26). The static component dK_{ys} of the field intensity dK_y at the point (a, y_2) induced by the current I_1, flowing in the element dy_1, is determined by the equation

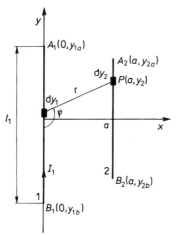

Fig. 4.26 Sketch illustrating the principle of calculating the mutual impedance of cables of finite length

$$dK_{ys} = I_1 \frac{\partial^2 q(r)}{\partial x^2} dy_1,$$ (4.32)

where

$$r = \sqrt{a^2 + (y_2 - y_1)^2},$$ (4.33)

$$q(r) = \frac{1}{2\pi \gamma_{er} r}.$$ (4.34)

After carrying out appropriate calculations, substitutions and transformations, we obtain the formula (4.40) for the value of the field intensity K_{ys} resulting from the flow of current I_1 in the conductor 1:

$$dK_{ys} = I_1 \frac{2r^2 - 3a^2}{r^5} dy_1,$$ (4.35)

$$y_1 - y_2 = a \cot \psi,$$ (4.36)

$$dy_1 = -a \frac{d\psi}{\sin^2 \psi},$$ (4.37)

$$dK_{ys} = I_1 \frac{2\sin \psi - 3\sin^3 \psi}{2\pi \gamma_{er} a^2} d\psi,$$ (4.38)

$$K_{ys} = I_1 \int_{\psi_A}^{\psi_B} \frac{2\sin \psi - 3\sin^3 \psi}{2\pi \gamma_{er} a^2} d\psi,$$ (4.39)

$$K_{ys} = \frac{I_1}{2\pi\gamma_{er}a^2}(\cos\psi_A - \cos\psi_B - \cos^3\psi_A + \cos^3\psi_B), \tag{4.40}$$

where

$$\cos\psi_A = \frac{y_{1a} - y_2}{\sqrt{a^2 + (y_{1a} - y_2)^2}}, \tag{4.41}$$

$$\cos\psi_B = \frac{y_{1b} - y_2}{\sqrt{a^2 + (y_{1b} - y)^2}}. \tag{4.42}$$

The induced component dK_{yi} of the field dK_y at the point $P(a, y_2)$, induced by the current I_1 flowing in the element dy_1 (Fig. 4.26), is determined by the equations

$$dK_{yi} = -I_1 P(r)dy_1, \tag{4.43}$$

$$P(r) = \frac{1}{2\pi\gamma_{er}} \frac{1 - (1 + kr)e^{-kr}}{r^3} \tag{4.44}$$

and

$$K_{yi} = \int_{y_{1b}}^{y_{1a}} dK_{yi} = I_1 \int_{y_{1b}}^{y_{1a}} \frac{1 - (1 + kr)e^{-kr}}{r^3} dy_1. \tag{4.45}$$

The integral (4.45) requires calculation by numerical methods. As an example the calculated values K_{ys} and K_{yi}, for a conductivity value γ_{er} of 0.1 S/m as previously assumed, for wire 1 having a length equal to 100 m ($y_{1a} = 0$, $y_{1b} = 100$ m), the distance between the wires (a) equal to 1 m and a 1 A current (I_1) in wire 1, are presented in Figs. 4.27 and 4.28.

The current I_1 flowing in conductor 1 induces in the circuit conductor 2–earth an electromotive force comprising two components: E_i resulted by mutual inductance and E_c—by coupling conductance:

$$E_i = \int_{y_{2b}}^{y_{2a}} K_{yi}dy_2, \tag{4.46}$$

$$E_c = \int_{y_{2b}}^{y_{2a}} K_{ys}dy_2. \tag{4.47}$$

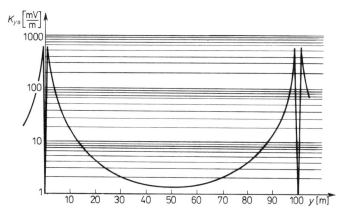

Fig. 4.27 Example of the distribution of the static component of the field, parallel to the conductor axis 1 ($l_1 = 100$ m, $I_1 = 1$ A), see Fig. 4.23

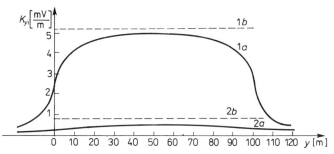

Fig. 4.28 Example of the distribution of the induced component of the field parallel to conductor 1 ($I_1 = 1$ A), 100 m long (1a imaginary component, 2a real component) and a conductor of infinite length (1b imaginary component, 2b real component)

As K_{ys} is the intensity of a potential field, the value of the integral (4.47) does not depend on the path of integration and is equal to the difference in scalar potentials at the points B_2 and A_2 (Fig. 4.26).

The scalar potential of the point P in the field produced by conductor 1 is described by the equation [45]:

$$V = \frac{I_1}{2\pi\gamma_{er}}\left(\frac{1}{r_a} - \frac{1}{r_b}\right), \tag{4.48}$$

where r_a and r_b are the distances between the point $P(a, y_2)$ and the two ends of conductor 1, and I_1 is the current flowing in this conductor.

Figure 4.29 presents the diagram of the equipotential lines for the case, when the length of the conductor 1 conducting a current of 1 A equals 100 m (conductivity $\gamma_{er} = 0.1$ S/m).

The magnetic interaction of conductors 1 and 2 with finite lengths shall be considered for two cases:

(a) conductor 2 with both ends earthed,

(b) conductor 2 with ends not earthed.

In case (a) the effect of the interaction between conductors 1 and 2 depends on the resultant electromotive force E

$$E = E_i + E_c. \tag{4.49}$$

In case (b) the effect of the interaction on the conductor 2 depends only on the component E_i.

Earthing conductor 2 close to the earthing points of conductor 1 may cause an increase in magnetic interaction, due to the influence of E_c. In the case of the examples presented in Figs. 4.27, 4.28 and 4.29, earthing conductor 2 at a distance of 2.5 m from conductor 1 will produce an electromotive force with component $E_i = 450$ mV and $E_c \approx 1200$ mV.

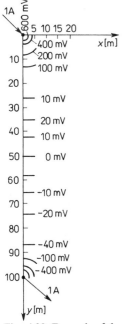

Fig. 4.29 Example of the distribution of the scalar potential on the surface of the ground for conductor 1 ($l_1 = 100$ m, $I_1 = 1$ A)

4.9   The influence of rails on the mutual impedance

Electric traction traffic rails belong to the class of earth return circuits which have conductors in contact with the ground (Fig. 4.30). The flow of currents in the rails and their potentials depend on the propagation coefficient Γ_r and on the impedance Z_{wr} of the rail-ground circuit. The propagation coefficient Γ_r can be calculated approximately from equation [16]:

$$\Gamma_r\left(Y_{ir}^{-1}+\frac{1}{\pi\gamma_{er}}\ln\frac{1.12}{r_s\sqrt{\Gamma_r^2+k^2}}\right)=Z_{ir}+\frac{j\omega\mu_0}{\pi}\ln\frac{1.12}{r_s\sqrt{\Gamma_r^2+k^2}}, \quad (4.50)$$

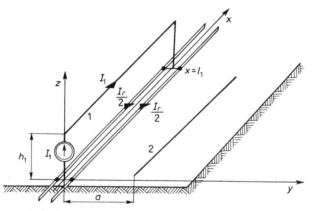

Fig. 4.30 Sketch illustrating the influence of a traction line upon an earth return circuit

where
  Z_{ir}—internal impedance of the rail per unit length,
  Y_{ir}—leakage admittance of the rail per unit length (assumes the value of 0.2–2.5 S/km [16]),
  r_s—substitute radius of the two-rail-system.
  The internal impedance of the rails per unit length is given by the relationship

$$Z_{ir}=\frac{1}{2u}\sqrt{\frac{\mu_r\mu_0}{\gamma_r}}(1+j\cdot0.6), \quad (4.51)$$

where
  u—cross-sectional perimeter of the rail,

μ_r—relative magnetic permeability of the rail,
γ_r—conductivity of the rail.
Figure 4.31 presents an example of the relationships between the specific internal impedance Z_{ir} of the rail and the frequency. The substitute radius of the rail is determined from the relationship

$$r_s = \sqrt{a_r r} \, , \qquad (4.52)$$

where $r = u/2\pi$, and a_r—distance between the rails.

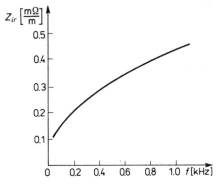

Fig. 4.31 Modulus of elementary internal impedance (per unit length) Z_{ir} of the rails (track) as a function of frequency f, for $u = 0.4$ m, $\mu_r = 400$

Equation (4.50) can be solved by the iterative method. The wave (characteristic) impedance of the rail-ground circuit is determined from the relationship

$$Z_{wr} = \sqrt{\frac{Z_r}{Y_r}} \, , \qquad (4.53)$$

where Z_r is the self-impedance of the rail, equal to

$$Z_r = Z_{ir} + j\frac{\omega\mu_0}{\pi} \ln \frac{1.12}{r_s\sqrt{\Gamma_r^2 + k^2}} \qquad (4.54)$$

and Y_r is the self-admittance of the rail-ground circuit, equal to

$$Y_r = \frac{1}{\dfrac{1}{Y_{ir}} + \dfrac{1}{\pi\gamma_{er}} \ln \dfrac{1.12}{r_s\sqrt{\gamma_r^2 + k^2}}} \, . \qquad (4.55)$$

Figures 4.32 and 4.33 present examples of the variation of Γ_r and Z_{wr} with the frequency, calculated according to (4.50)–(4.55) for values of $u = 0.4$ m, $\gamma_{er} = 0.1$ S/m, $\mu_r = 400$, $a_r = 1$ m, $Y_r^{-1} = 0$, $Y_{ir}^{-1} = 400$ $\Omega\cdot$m. Assuming an infinite rail length, the system of Fig. 4.30 can be considered to represent the superposition of four elementary systems, in which the ground-rail circuit is energized both conductively (by the current) and inductively [16]—Fig. 4.34.

In practice it is assumed that the rails can be treated as infinitely long if their length extending beyond the supply zone is equal to at least $3/\mathrm{Re}\Gamma_r$. Using the equations for the currents and potentials in the rails we obtain [16] the following equations describing the currents I_r and the potentials V_r for the system presented in Fig. 4.30:

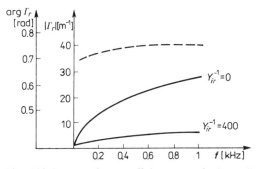

Fig. 4.32 Propagation coefficient Γ_r of the rails (track) as a function of frequency f; —— modulus Γ_r, ------ argument Γ_r

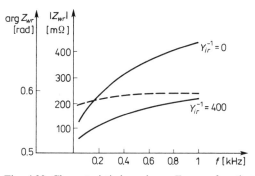

Fig. 4.33 Characteristic impedance Z_{wr} as a function of frequency f, —— modulus Z_{wr}, ------ argument Z_{wr}

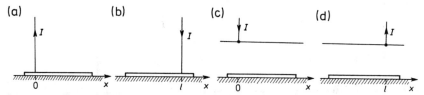

Fig. 4.34 Schematic basic systems for the case of an infinite length of rails of the system in Fig. 4.30; (a), (b) current supply; (c), (d) inductive supply

$$I_r(x) = 0.5\,I_1 \left\{ -\text{sign}(x) \left[e^{-\Gamma_r|x|} + \frac{Z_{1r}}{Z_r}\left(1 - e^{-\Gamma_r|x|}\right) \right] + \right.$$
$$\left. + \text{sign}(x-1) \left[e^{-\Gamma_r|x-1|} + \frac{Z_{1r}}{Z_r}\left(1 - e^{-\Gamma_r|x-1|}\right) \right] \right\}, \tag{4.56}$$

$$V_r = 0.5\,I_1\,Z_{wr}\left(1 - \frac{Z_{1r}}{Z_r}\right)\left(e^{-\Gamma_r|x-1|} - e^{-\Gamma_r|x|}\right), \tag{4.57}$$

where Z_{1r} is the mutual impedance of the contact wire-ground and rail-ground circuits. At points far removed from the ends of the supply zone, i.e. for the condition

$$\frac{3}{\text{Re}\,\Gamma_r} < x < l - \frac{3}{\text{Re}\,\Gamma_r} \tag{4.58}$$

equations (4.56) and (4.57) can be simplified to the forms

$$I_r(x) = -I_1\frac{Z_{1r}}{Z_r}, \qquad V_r(x) = 0.$$

Examples of the variations of the potentials and currents of the rails, calculated according to equations (4.56) and (4.57) are presented in Figs. 4.35 and 4.36.

The electromotive force of the resultant interaction between the electric traction line and wire 2 is equal to

$$E_{it} = (I_1 Z_{12} + \overline{I}_r Z_{r2})l_2, \tag{4.59}$$

where

Z_{r2} — mutual impedance of rail-wire 2,
$\overline{I}_r$ — averaged current in the rails, and
l_2 — length of wire 2.

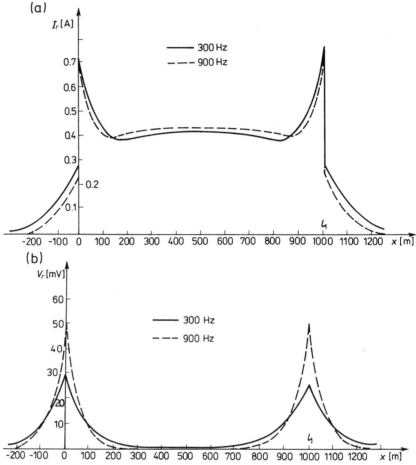

Fig. 4.35 Example of distribution of: (a) currents and (b) rail potentials for the case of a traction line of a length $l_1 = 1000$ m ($\gamma_{er} = 0.1$ S/m, $h_1 = 2$ m, $u = 0.4$ m, $a = 1$ m, $I_1 = 1$ A, $Y_{ir}^{-1} = 0$)

If wire 2 is placed in the zone meeting condition (4.58), equation (4.59) can be reduced to the form

$$E_{it} = I_1 Z_{12} r_r l_2,$$ (4.60)

where r_r represents a rail reduction coefficient (screening factor), equal to

$$r_r = 1 - \frac{Z_{1r} Z_{r2}}{Z_r Z_{12}}.$$ (4.61)

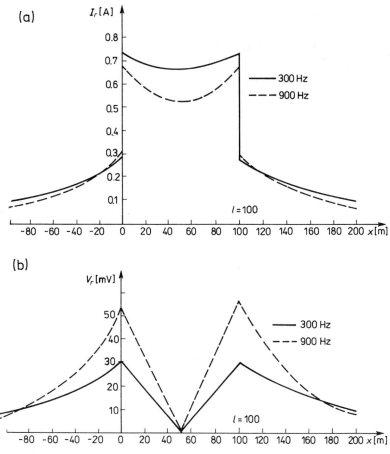

Fig. 4.36 Example of the distribution as in Fig. 4.35, but for a length $l_1 = 100$ m

Figure 4.37 presents examples of the results of measuring the relationship between r_r and the distance a between the rails and influenced lines for Soviet railways [34]. In the case where the ends of wire 2 are not earthed, the interaction of the electric traction circuit wire 2 is caused by the formation of the electromotive force E_{it} as determined from equation (4.59). If the ends of the wire 2 are earthed (or connected to the rails) the interaction is caused by the formation of an electromotive force E_{it} and the difference in potentials ΔU between the earthing points (or points where the ends are connected to the rails) of wire 2.

Connecting the wire to the rails may cause a substantial increase in interaction. In the case where the ends of wire 2 are earthed at a certain distance from the rails a conductance coupling may occur, similar to the case of wire 1 with ends earthed (Fig. 4.26).

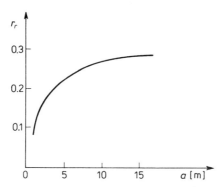

Fig. 4.37 Rail reduction coefficient r_r in function of distance a

4.10 The mutual inductance of earth return circuits in headings

In dog headings we have a system comprising two environments (air, rock mass with lining), whose shapes are determined by the cross-section of the heading. In such a system, the assumptions made while introducing equation (4.25) are not met. Only in the case where the distance between wires 1 and 2 and the side walls and the roof, and the distance between wires 1 and 2 are small, does equation (4.25) allow the mutual impedance to be assessed, with a degree of approximation (similar to the case of electric interactions).

In dog headings, one usually finds a number of long metallic elements, which are earthed either on purpose or accidentally, for example cable armouring, pipelines, ropes or rails of neighbouring tracks. The currents flowing in the earthed elements interact with wire 2, in similar fashion to the currents flowing in the rails of the electric traction line as described in the previous section. This phenomenon is taken into consideration by introducing the reduction coefficient of metallic elements r_m [28].

The resultant electromotive force E_{ih} due to a magnetic coupling in a dog heading is determined by the equation

$$E_{ih} = I_1 Z_{12} l_2 r_r r_m = j\omega I_1 M_{12} l_2 r_r r_m. \qquad (4.62)$$

The quantity $M_{12h} = M_{12}r_r r_m$ is called the *resultant mutual inductance* of the electric traction line 1 and the wire 2 in a dog heading.

It is difficult to measure the value M_{12} in a dog heading, as it is necessary to either eliminate or take into account the coefficients r_r and r_m. It is easier to measure the resultant mutual inductance M_{12h}. Figure 4.25 presents an example of measurements of the resultant mutual inductance M_{12h} in an experimental drift, 70 meters long. It is difficult to directly compare the M_{12h} values measured in the drift with the M_{12} values calculated from equation (4.25), as the values of the parameters r_r, r_m and γ_{er} are not known. The presence of metallic objects decreases the value of the mutual inductance. A similar effect is produced by an increase in earth conductivity γ_{er}. In some situations, the presence of metallic elements is taken into account by assuming an appropriately high earth conductivity (e.g. 0.2–1 $S \cdot m^{-1}$ for urban areas [28]). Since the values of M_{12h} measured in the drift correspond to within a few tens of percent of the calculated values of M_{12}, and, the ratio M_{12h}/M_{12} represents a realistic value of $r_r r_m$, we can assume that there is satisfactory agreement between the measurements and the results of the calculations.

4.11   The magnetic interaction between a traction (contact) line and an earth return circuit

The interaction between the electric traction line 1 and an earth return circuit (line), comprising the wire 2 and loaded with the impedances Z_a and Z_b has been analysed with the assumption that the distance between the ends of the wire 2 and the ends of the electric traction line supply zone is greater than $3/\text{Re}\Gamma_r$ (Fig. 4.38). The line 2 shall be treated as a system with distributed parameters, a longitudinal one Z and a transverse one Y. The longitudinal impedance of line 2 per unit length is determined by the following equation [16]:

$$Z = Z_{in} + Z_{ex}, \tag{4.63}$$

where

   Z_{in} — internal impedance of wire 2, and
   Z_{ex} — external impedance of line 2 (wire 2—ground).

The internal impedance per unit length of wire 2 with a radius r_0 is equal to

$$Z_{in} = R_{in} + j\omega L_{in} = j\frac{\omega\mu_w}{2\pi r_0 k_w}\frac{I_0(k_w r_0)}{I_1(k_w r_0)}, \tag{4.64}$$

where

I_0, I_1 — modified Bessel's function of the first kind, of the zero and
    first order,

$k_w - \sqrt{j\omega\mu_w\gamma_w}$,
μ_w — magnetic permeability of wire 2,
γ_w — conductivity of the wire 2.

If $k_w r_0 > 10$, equation (4.64) can be reduced to the form [16]:·

$$Z_{in} = \frac{k_w r_0}{2\sqrt{2}}R_0 + j\frac{0.2\sqrt{2}\,\mu_w\omega}{k_w r_0} = R_{in} + j\omega L_{in}, \tag{4.65}$$

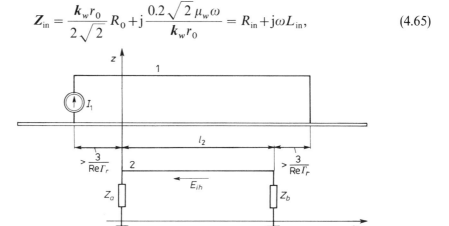

Fig. 4.38 Schematic systems: 1—of a traction line, 2—of an earth return circuit

where R_0 is the specific resistance of the wire per unit length for a direct
current. In the case of a copper wire with a diameter of 0.8 mm, and
for frequencies lower than 30 kHz, the specific resistance is equal
to $R_{in} = 35$ mΩ/m, and the internal inductance per unit length L_{in}
$= 125$ nH/m.

The internal resistance R_t and inductivity L_t of wire armouring
(banding steel) at a frequency of 50 Hz are equal to [27]:

$$R_t = \frac{49D}{a^2 b} \times 10^{-9}\,\frac{\Omega}{m}, \tag{4.66a}$$

$$L_t = \frac{4\pi mbn}{D}\mu_r \times 10^{-7}\,\frac{H}{m}, \tag{4.66b}$$

where
   D — outer diameter of cable armouring,
   a, b — width and thickness of armouring band,
$$m = \frac{a}{a+c},$$
   c — spacing between the bands,
   n — number of bands,
   μ_r — relative magnetic permeability of steel. For cable armouring it
      is assumed that $100 < \mu_r < 400$ [27].

Substituting the parameters of telephone cables used in mining (e.g.
$a = 35$ mm, $b = 0.5$ mm, $c = 10$ mm, $\mu_r = 200$, $D = 15$ mm) into
equation (4.66) we obtain $R_t = 5.1$ mΩ/m and $L_t = 14$ μH/m.

The calculation of the internal impedance of the cable armouring for
frequencies higher than 50 Hz requires that the spiral flow of the current
in the armouring be taken into account. From an analysis of the
electromagnetic field in a spiral lead [27], it appears that the internal
impedance per unit length of a spiral core is equal to the sum of the
internal impedances of a tube with dimensions equal to those of a spiral
core and the internal impedance of a tube with a radius smaller by
a factor of $1/\sin^2 \vartheta$ than the radius of a spiral core (ϑ — the angle of band
winding in the armouring).

The internal impedance of a tube with the outer radius r_0 and
thickness T is equal to [46]

$$Z_{in} = \frac{1}{2\pi r_0 \gamma_w} k_w \coth k_w T. \tag{4.67}$$

The external impedance of the cable is determined by the equation
[16]

$$Z_{ex} = \frac{\omega \mu_0}{\pi} \left[Q(2h', 0) + j \frac{1}{2} \ln \frac{2h}{r_0} \right], \tag{4.68}$$

where
   μ_0 — magnetic permeability of the earth (rock),
   h' — hk,
   h — height at which cable is suspended above to floor.
For $h' \leqslant 0.05$ equation (4.68) can be reduced to the form

$$Z_{ex} = R_{ex} + j\omega L_{ex} = \frac{\omega \mu_0}{8} + j\omega \frac{\mu_0}{2\pi} \ln \frac{1.85}{kr_0}, \tag{4.69}$$

where

$$R_{ex} = \frac{\omega\mu_0}{8} \text{---resistance of the earth (rock) per unit length}$$

$$L_{ex} = \frac{\mu_0}{2\pi} \ln \frac{1.85}{kr_0} \text{---external inductance of wire 2 per unit length.}$$

Figure 4.39 presents the frequency characteristics of the external inductance L_{ex} and the earth resistance R_{ex}.

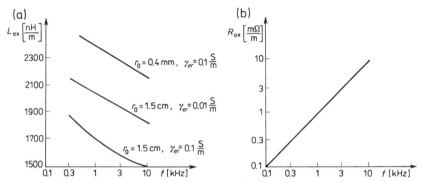

Fig. 4.39 Frequency characteristics of: (a) external inductance L_{ex}, (b) earth resistance R_{ex}

The transverse admittance per unit length of the communication line is determined by the equation (if leakage is disregarded):

$$Y = j\omega \frac{2\pi\varepsilon_0}{\text{arcosh}\left(\dfrac{h}{r_0}\right)}, \tag{4.70}$$

where $\varepsilon_0 = 8.85 \times 10^{-12}$ F/m is the dielectric permeability of a vacuum.

The analysis of circuits with distributed parameters is carried out by dividing the circuit into intervals of infinitesimal length.

The diagram of an element of infinitesimal length of an earth return circuit subjected to inductive interaction is presented in Fig. 4.40.

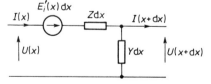

Fig. 4.40 Infinitesimal section of an earth return circuit in an external magnetic field

An infinitesimal length of the communication line is described by the following equations:

$$\frac{dU(x)}{dx} + ZI(x) = E'_i(x),$$ (4.71a)

$$\frac{dI}{dx} = YU(x)$$ (4.71b)

where $E'_i(x)$—elementary (unity) electromotive force per unit length induced in wire 2.

The solution of equations (4.71) takes the form [36]:

$$U(x) = F_1(x) + F_2(x) + ge^{-\Gamma x} + de^{\Gamma x},$$ (4.72a)

$$I(x) = \frac{1}{Z_w}[F_1(x) - F_2(x) + ge^{-\Gamma x} - de^{\Gamma x}].$$ (4.72b)

The functions $F_1(x)$ and $F_2(x)$ assume the form
(a) for $E'_i(x) \neq \text{const}$

$$F_1(x) = 0.5e^{-\Gamma x} \int_0^x e^{\Gamma x} E'_i(x)dx,$$ (4.73a)

$$F_2(x) = 0.5e^{\Gamma x} \int_0^x e^{-\Gamma x} E'_i(x)dx;$$ (4.73b)

(b) for $E'_i(x) = E'_i = \text{const}$

$$F_1(x) = \frac{E'_i}{2\Gamma}(1 - e^{-\Gamma x}),$$ (4.74a)

$$F_2(x) = \frac{E'_i}{2\Gamma}(e^{\Gamma x} - 1),$$ (4.74b)

where
$\Gamma = \alpha + j\beta = \sqrt{ZY}$ — the propagation constant of the line,
$\qquad \alpha$ — wave attenuation constant of the line,
$\qquad \beta$ — phase constant of the line,

$$Z_w = \sqrt{\frac{Z}{Y}} \text{ — wave impedance of the line.}$$

If a line of length l is loaded with the impedance Z_a and Z_b (Fig. 4.38), the constants g and d are determined by the relationships

$$g = \frac{Q_1}{2N}(Z_w - Z_a), \tag{4.75a}$$

$$d = -\frac{Q_1}{2N}(Z_w + Z_a), \tag{4.75b}$$

$$N = (Z_f^2 + Z_a Z_b)\sinh\Gamma l + Z_w(Z_a + Z_b)\cos\Gamma l, \tag{4.75c}$$

$$Q_1 = Z_w[F_1(l) + F_2(l)] - Z_b[F_1(l) - F_2(l)]. \tag{4.75d}$$

Figure 4.41 presents an example of the frequency characteristics of wave parameters calculated from equations (4.63), (4.67) and (4.68) for the values: $\gamma_{er} = 0.1$ S/m, $r_0 = 7.5$ mm, $h = 9$ mm, $\mu_r = 200$, $T = 0.5$ mm, $\sin^2\vartheta = 0.41$, and those measured for a cable of the type YTKGXFty ($5 \times 2 \times 0.8$ mm) located in a drift. The internal impedance of the

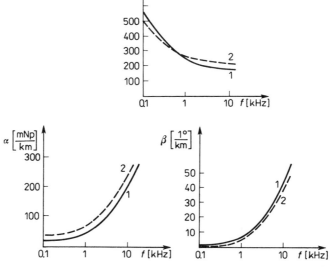

Fig. 4.41 Frequency characteristics of the wave parameters (Z_w, α, β) of an earth return circuit; 1—values calculated for $\gamma_{er} = 0.1$ S/m, $r_0 = 7.5$ mm, $h = 9$ mm, $T = 0.5$ mm, $\mu_r = 200$, $\sin^2\vartheta = 0.47$; 2—values measured for the cable YTKGXFty ($5 \times 2 \times 0.8$ mm) in a drift with arch support

armouring has been calculated by using the value for the substitute radius of a tube r_s, equal to

$$r_s = r_0 \frac{\sin^2 \vartheta}{1 + \sin^2 \vartheta},$$
(4.76)

in equation (4.67).

The results of the calculations are in good agreement with the results of the measurements. An agreement between the measurements and calculations of the transverse admittance of the track was obtained for a short distance between the cable and the side wall (equal to the thickness of the sheath).

Underground cable lines are built by connecting individual lengths of the cable using cable boxes or various types of joints (KVA, SOdt, SOmt). Armouring, which enters the joint or box, is earthed. This method of constructing a cable line reduces the length of the earth return circuit to a few hundreds of meters. Taking into account the possibility of accidental earthing of a cable armouring, it is clear that earth return lines in mines never exceed one kilometre in length.

The actual lengths of earth return tracks and wave attenuation constants allow us to reduce equation (4.72a) to the form

$$U(x) = -E_i' x + E_i' l \frac{(Z_x + Z_a)(1 + 0.5 Z_b Yl)}{Z_a + Z_b + Zl + Z_a Z_b Yl}.$$
(4.77)

The voltage across the terminals of an impedance $Z_a(x = 0)$ is equal to

$$U(0) = E_i' l \frac{Z_a(1 + 0.5 Z_b Yl)}{Z_a + Z_b + Zl + Z_a Z_b Yl}.$$
(4.78)

Equation (4.78) constitutes an approximate solution for an earth return line, whose substitute diagram is presented in Fig. 4.42. The voltage across the terminals of unloaded line ($Z_a = Z_b = \infty$) with low attenuation ($\Gamma l \ll 1$) is equal to

$$U(0) = 0.5 E_i' l.$$
(4.79)

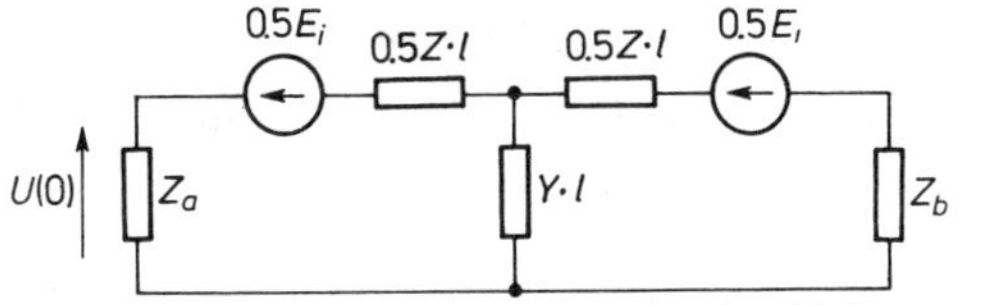

Fig. 4.42 Substitute system for a circuit with low attenuation in an external magnetic field ($\Gamma l \ll 1$)

4.12   The magnetic interaction between a traction line and a symmetrical line

For a section of infinitesimal length of a symmetrical circuit (line) loaded non-symmetrically, represented by a substitute diagram as in Fig. 4.43, we may write the following system of equations:

$$\frac{dU_1(x)}{dx} = -[E_i' dx + ZI_1(x) + Z_{12} I_2(x)], \tag{4.80a}$$

$$\frac{dU_2(x)}{dx} = -[E_i' dx + ZI_2(x) + Z_{12} I_1(x)], \tag{4.80b}$$

$$\frac{dI_1(x)}{dx} = -U_1(x)(Y + Y_{12}) + U_2 Y_{12}, \tag{4.80c}$$

$$\frac{dI_2(x)}{dx} = -U_2(x)(Y + Y_{12}) + U_1(x) Y_{12}, \tag{4.80d}$$

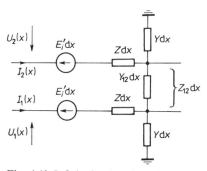

Fig. 4.43 Infinitesimal section of a symmetrical cable circuit in an external magnetic field

where

Z_{12}—mutual impedance per unit length of the two circuits; wire 1—earth and wire 2—earth,

Y_{12}—admittance per unit length between wires 1 and 2.

In further considerations, an ideal symmetry between the track and the earth and the electric traction network has been assumed (the electromotive forces induced in both wires are identical).

Using the substitutions

$$U_1(x) = U_i(x) + \tfrac{1}{2} U_r(x), \tag{4.81a}$$

$$U_2(x) = U_i(x) - \frac{1}{2} U_r(x),$$ (4.81b)

$$I_1(x) = \frac{1}{2} I_i(x) + I_r(x),$$ (4.81c)

$$I_2(x) = \frac{1}{2} I_i(x) - I_r(x),$$ (4.81d)

equations (4.80) are transformed into [31]:

$$\frac{dU_r(x)}{dx} = -Z_r I_r(x),$$ (4.82a)

$$\frac{dI_r(x)}{dx} = -Y_r U_r(x),$$ (4.82b)

$$\frac{dU_i(x)}{dx} = -[E'_i + Z_c I_i(x)],$$ (4.83a)

$$\frac{dI_i(x)}{dx} = -Y_c U_i(x),$$ (4.83b)

where

$Z_r = 2(Z - Z_{12})$—impedance per unit length of a differential line (symmetrical),

$Y_r = 0.5Y + Y_{12}$—admittance per unit length of a differential line (symmetrical),

$Z_c = \dfrac{Z + Z_{12}}{2}$—impedance per unit length of a common line (earth return),

$Y_c = 2Y$—admittance per unit length of a common line (earth return)

The transformations applied allow us to substitute a symmetrical line with the superposition of a common and differential one. Only the common line is subjected to the inductive interaction while both lines load each other through a closing four-terminal network [31]. An example of a substitute diagram for a symmetrical track loaded asymmetrically is presented in Fig. 4.44. After disregarding the longi-

tudinal impedances, we obtain the solution for the system presented in
Fig. 4.44 in the form

$$U(0) = \frac{1}{2} E'_i l \frac{Y}{Y + Y_{12} + \dfrac{1}{Z_a} + \dfrac{1}{Z_b}}. \qquad (4.84)$$

The analysis of magnetic interaction upon a symmetrical line
presented above gives correct results for the case of high load asymmetry
as for example in Fig. 4.44a. In the case of low load asymmetry we have
to take the line asymmetry into account.

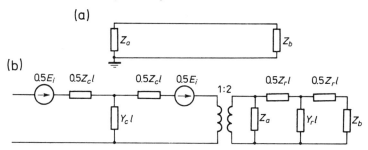

Fig. 4.44 Diagrams: (a) schematic and (b) substitute of a symmetric circuit asymmetrically
loaded in an external magnetic field

From the point of view of magnetic interactions upon a symmetrical
line which is symmetrically loaded we shall differentiate
 — lines with parallel cores (uncompensated length of an overhead
   track),
 — symmetrical lines with twisted cores (cable lines).
In overhead lines, magnetic interaction causes the excitation of different
electromotive forces in the two cores, due to the difference in distance
between the cores and the traction line. This is called a direct interaction
[81]. Direct magnetic interaction does not occur in mine headings and
will therefore not be discussed.

In cable lines, it is assumed that an identical electromotive force E'_i is
being induced in each core, and the reason for the appearance of voltages
at the final terminals of a line is due to randomly distributed asymmetry
along the line and impedance asymmetry at the line terminals.

If we take line asymmetry into account, equations (4.82) and (4.83)
assume the following form:

$$\frac{dU_r(x)}{dx} = -Z_r I_r(x) - \Delta Z I_i(x), \tag{4.85a}$$

$$\frac{dI_r(x)}{dx} = -Y_r U_r(x) - \Delta Y U_i(x), \tag{4.85b}$$

$$\frac{dU_i(x)}{dx} = -Z_c I_i(x) - \Delta Z I_r(x) - E'_i, \tag{4.85c}$$

$$\frac{dI_i(x)}{dx} = -Y_c U_i(x) - \Delta Y U_r(x), \tag{4.85d}$$

where

ΔY—transverse asymmetry per unit length of the line, mostly resulting from asymmetry of the core to earth capacity of both cores, i.e.

$$\Delta Y = \frac{j\omega(C_1 - C_2)}{2},$$

ΔZ—longitudinal asymmetry per unit length of the line most often being the result of the difference in the resistance of the cores, i.e.

$$|\Delta Z| = \tfrac{1}{2}(R_1 - R_2).$$

These equations describe the system comprising a common and a differential line, however only a common track is subjected to inductive interaction. A differential line is coupled with the common line through longitudinal asymmetry ΔZ and through transverse asymmetry ΔY; these asymmetries are randomly distributed along the line.

In practice, the influence of line asymmetry is accounted for by introducing a line susceptibility to magnetic interaction coefficient λ_m, defined as [28, 81]

$$\lambda_m = \frac{E_p}{E_i}, \tag{4.86}$$

where

E_p—transverse electromotive force excited in a line equal to double the value of the voltage at the terminals of a wave-loaded line,

E_i—longitudinal electromotive force excited in a line, equal to $E_i = E'_i \cdot l$.

The coefficient λ_m can be determined from the equation [1]:

$$\lambda_m = \frac{\omega \Delta C_l \sqrt{600 Z_a}}{4} \sqrt{\frac{1}{\alpha l} \left[(1 - e^{-2\alpha l}) \left(\frac{1}{2} + \frac{1}{\alpha^2 l^2} \right) - \frac{1}{\alpha l} (1 + e^{-2\alpha l}) \right]},$$

(4.87)

where ΔC_l is the earth return capacitive asymmetry of a line of length l. The capacitive asymmetry ΔC_l of a cable lines is a function of cable length. For mining cables the relation between the capacitive asymmetry and the length l is determined as follows [32]:

$$\Delta C_l = \frac{1}{2} \Delta C_{600} \left(\frac{l}{600} + \frac{\sqrt{l}}{600} \right),$$

(4.88)

where ΔC_{600} is the capacitive asymmetry of a cable line of 600 m length.

Another method of calculating the magnetic interaction is presented in [2]. There, a line loaded at the points A and B is considered, which consists of 3 elements of lengths l_1, l_2, l_3, of which the length l_2 is subjected to magnetic interaction exciting the longitudinal electromotive force E_j. The voltage U_A (across the impedance Z_a terminating the line) is determined from the relationships,

$$U_A = 2E_i \sqrt{\lambda P_A Z_a + (g_{uB} u)^2 + [g_{uB}(1-u)]^2 \, e^{-2\alpha S_1 (1 + v_1 + v_3)}},$$

$$P_A = u^2 v_1 e^{-\alpha S_2 v_1} + \left(u^2 - u + \frac{1}{3} \right) e^{-\alpha S_2 (1 + 2v_1)} +$$

$$+ (1-u)^2 v_3 e^{-\alpha l_2 (v_3 + 2v_1 + 2)},$$

(4.89)

$$u = \frac{0.5 + v_3}{1 + v_1 + v_2},$$

$$v_1 = \frac{l_1}{l_2},$$

$$v_3 = \frac{l_3}{l_2},$$

$$\lambda = \left(\omega \frac{\Delta C}{\sqrt{l_1 + l_2 + l_3}} \right)^2 \frac{Z_w l_2}{16},$$

where g_{uA} and g_{uB} is the line load asymmetry at the points A and B, and ΔC is the capacitive asymmetry of the line.

However, in cable lines, in which the cores are located inside a conducting sheath of armouring, there are two cores (1 and 2) and a sheath (3). In such a case equations (4.82) and (4.83) take the form:

$$\frac{d[U]}{dx} = -[Z] \times [I] + [E'], \tag{4.90a}$$

$$\frac{d[I]}{dx} = -[Y] \times [U], \tag{4.90b}$$

where

$$[U] = [U_1\, U_2\, U_3]^\mathrm{T} \text{— vector of voltages relative to earth,}$$
$$[I] = [I_1\, I_2\, I_3]^\mathrm{T} \text{— vector of currents,}$$

$$[Z] = \begin{bmatrix} Z_{11} & Z_{22} & Z_{13} \\ Z_{21} & Z_{22} & Z_{23} \\ Z_{32} & Z_{32} & Z_{33} \end{bmatrix} \text{— impedance matrix}$$

$$[Y] = \begin{bmatrix} Y_{11} & Y_{12} & Y_{13} \\ Y_{21} & Y_{22} & Y_{23} \\ Y_{31} & Y_{32} & Y_{33} \end{bmatrix} \text{— admittance matrix,}$$

$Z_{i,j}(i \neq j)$ — mutual impedance per unit length,
$Z_{i,i}$ — self-impedance per unit length,
$Y_{i,i}$ — self-admittance per unit length,
$Y_{i,j}(i \neq j)$ — mutual admittance per unit length,
$E' = [E'_i\, E'_i\, E'_i]^\mathrm{T}$ — electromotive force per unit length induced in both cores of the track (1, 2) and the sheath (3) of the line.

Making the following substitution:

$$U_1 = U_p + U_d + 0.5U_s,$$
$$U_2 = U_p + U_d - 0.5U_s,$$
$$U_3 = U_p,$$
$$I_1 = 0.5I_d + I_s,$$
$$I_2 = 0.5I_d - I_s,$$
$$I_3 = I_p - I_d,$$

we obtain

$$\frac{d}{dx}\begin{bmatrix} U_s \\ U_d \\ U_p \end{bmatrix} = -\begin{bmatrix} Z_s & \Delta Z & 0 \\ \Delta Z & Z_d & Z_t \\ 0 & Z_t & Z_p \end{bmatrix} \times \begin{bmatrix} I_s \\ I_d \\ I_p \end{bmatrix} + \begin{bmatrix} 0 \\ 0 \\ E_i' \end{bmatrix}, \tag{4.91a}$$

$$\frac{d}{dx}\begin{bmatrix} I_s \\ I_d \\ I_p \end{bmatrix} = -\begin{bmatrix} Y_s & \Delta Y & 0 \\ \Delta Y & Y_d & 0 \\ 0 & 0 & Y_p \end{bmatrix} \times \begin{bmatrix} U_s \\ U_d \\ U_p \end{bmatrix}, \tag{4.91b}$$

where

ΔZ—longitudinal asymmetry of a symmetrical circuit,

ΔY—transverse asymmetry of a symmetrical circuit,

Z_t—transfer impedance between the outer circuit (sheath (3) earth) and inner circuit (cores (1, 2)—sheath (3)).

The above equations describe a system of three circuits (lines):

a symmetrical circuit (line) (cores 1, 2) with the parameters Z_s, Y_s,

an inner circuit (line) (cores-sheath)—Z_d, Y_d, and

an outer circuit (line) (sheath-earth)—Z_p, Y_p.

The electromotive force E_i is being induced in the outer circuit only, producing there the current I_p. In the inner circuit, the current I_a produces a voltage equal to $I_p Z_t$ which is lower than E_i due to the screening action of the sheath (armouring). The symmetrical circuit is coupled with the inner circuit through transverse and longitudinal asymmetry.

Loading the line at its end may be described by the following parameters (Fig. 4.45): impedance Z_A (for the differential current), impedance Z_{AW} (for the common current), and asymmetry relative to earth A_A.

A symmetrical line, subjected to a magnetic interaction, may be characterized by the following parameters (Fig. 4.45): input impedance Z_T, input impedance for the common current Z_{TW}, asymmetry relative to earth A_T, transverse electromotive force E_p, and common electromotive force E_{ws}.

An analysis of the system presented in Fig. 4.45 yields the following solution [31]:

$$U_A = E_p \frac{Z_A}{Z_T + Z_A} + \frac{1}{2} E_{ws} \frac{Z_T Z_A (A_A - A_T)}{(Z_T + Z_A)(Z_{TW} + Z_{AW})}. \tag{4.92}$$

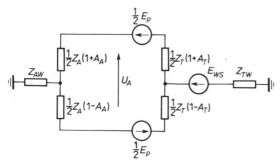

Fig. 4.45 Substitute diagram of the influence of the asymmetry of terminating impedance and the asymmetry of the wire circuit in an external magnetic field onto the transverse voltage U_A

The second component of equation (4.92) describes the transformation of the asymmetric electromotive force (E_{ws}) into a transverse voltage caused by a line asymmetry and asymmetry of the load impedance. Earthing of the cable armouring (or that of a conducting sheath) influences the interaction between the traction line and a cable line.

The current I_1 in a contact (trolley) wire causes the formation of a longitudinal electromotive force E_{ih} in the line and in the armouring (Fig. 4.46). The electromotive force E_{ih} excited in the armouring-earth circuit induces a current I_p in the armouring, which is given by the equation

$$I_p = \frac{E_{ih}}{Z_p l_2 Z_{ua} + Z_{ub}},$$

(4.93)

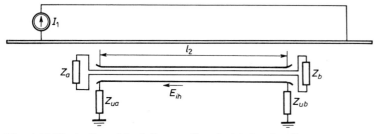

Fig. 4.46 Illustration of the influence of an electric traction line upon a symmetric wire circuit in a cable with conductive covering (screen, armouring).

where

Z_p — impedance (per unit length) of the armouring-earth circuit,

Z_{ua}, Z_{ub} — impedance of armouring earthing.

The current I_p induces the longitudinal electromotive force E_{wp} in the line, as determined by the relationship

$$E_{wp} = Z_{pT} I_p l, \tag{4.94}$$

where Z_{pT} is the transfer impedance of the armouring-earth and the inner core-earth circuit.

The magnetic flux produced in the armouring-earth circuit, is totally coupled with the inner core-earth circuit, and Z_{pT} is equal to the reactance of the armouring-earth circuit, i.e.

$$Z_{pT} = I_m Z_p. \tag{4.95}$$

The resultant longitudinal electromotive force in the line is equal to

$$E_{ic} = E_{iu} - E_{wp} = E_{ih}\left(1 - \frac{\text{Im}Z_p l}{Z_p l + Z_{ua} + Z_{ub}}\right). \tag{4.96}$$

In the case of low impedances of armouring earthing ($Z_{ua} \ll Z_p l$, $Z_{ub} \ll Z_p l$), equation (4.94) is reduced to the form

$$E_{ic} = E_{ih}\frac{\text{Re}Z_p}{Z_p} = E_{ih}r_k, \tag{4.97}$$

where $r_k = \dfrac{\text{Re}Z_p}{|Z_p|}$ is the screening factor of the cable armouring. The

reduction coefficient r_k is equal to the ratio of the value of the longitudinal electromotive force (per unit length) in the line, to the value of the longitudinal electromotive force in this line with no metallic sheath or armouring present.

For cables with armouring consisting of steel elements (wires, tapes) the magnetic permeability and the internal impedance of the armouring, are functions of the current flowing in the armouring. In practice, the influence of this current on the value r_k is taken into account by inserting the equation for r_k into the function of the longitudinal electromotive force induced in the armouring. The value of r_k depends on the structure of the cable. In certain situations, cables with reduced r_k value are being used. For mining purposes, the FfTKGXekwy cables have been

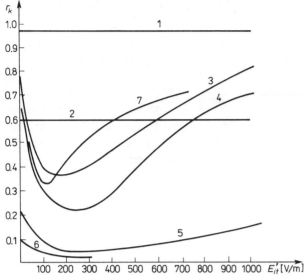

Fig. 4.47 Reduction coefficient of a cable r_k in function of the longitudinal electromotive force induced in a conductive covering E'_{it} (50 Hz): 1—lead covering with diameter $D = 20$ mm; 2—copper covering, $D = 20$ mm; 3—iron armouring strip, $D = 10$–20 mm; 4—iron armouring strip $D = 20$–35 mm; 5—aluminium sheath 1.6 mm thick (AlTKDkFty); 6—lead sheath 1.8 mm thick and wrapping of 10 copper bands 28×0.25 mm and iron armouring (Cables de Lyon); 7—FfTKGXekwy $30 \times 4 \times 0.8$ mm

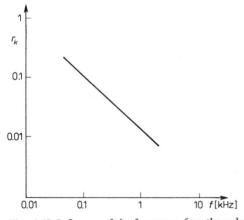

Fig. 4.48 Influence of the frequency f on the value of r_k

designed, where a reduction of the r_k value has been obtained by using a copper strip as taping.

Figure 4.47 shows the relationship between the coefficient r_k and the electromotive force in armouring or sheaths for various cable designs [23, 27, 83]. The value of r_k decreases with the increase in frequency. For cables with a lowered reduction coefficient, at a frequency of 800 Hz typical r_k values range from 0.005 to 0.02 [27]. An example of the relationship between r_k and the frequency for a current $I_p = 1$ A, flowing through a cable with aluminium sheath 1 mm thick, 14 mm in diameter and with armouring made of two steel bands with dimensions 35×0.8 mm, is presented (curve 5) in Fig. 4.48 [1].

5 Electromagnetic Interference in Mine Communications Networks

5.1 Communication and dispatching systems in underground mines

In underground coal mines various types of communication systems are used. These can be divided into three groups:
- all-mine telephone communication systems, using an automatic branch exchange serving both underground and surface telephones,
- local communication systems, in which loudspeaking devices, telephones and wireless devices are used within individual technological section like coal-faces, inclined drifts, belt conveyor routes, wheel transport routes,
- dispatch communication systems, which make it possible for other communication systems and devices to communicate with the dispatch centre or management in order to supervise the mining process or the evacuation of staff in case of emergency.

These systems are used under appropriate conditions and complement one another. The GST loudspeaking system for example enables the staff to transmit warning signals and in addition to speech, communication signals as well, so as to stop the machines and other equipment in case emergency. In dispatch communication networks, on the other hand, alarm loudspeaking systems (e.g. AUD-80) and dispatch telephone systems (e.g. UDG and UDK) are used. The reliable operation of all the various types of communication systems and the interference-free transmission of signals constitute the foundation of good control and management as well as of the safety of work in a mine.

5.1.1   Telephone communication

The *general (all-mine) telephone communication system* constitutes the basic element of communication by wire in a mine. This type of communication system uses a private branch exchange (PBX) with either crossbar switches (e.g. CKK) or with rotary selector switches (e.g. CAGK). All the connections coming from underground users are connected manually by the staff of the intermediate exchange, whereas the connnections coming from the surface to the underground workings may be effected either automatically (crossbar switch exchange) or manually (CAGK exchange).

In methane-free mines, telephones of the types KTA-3 and KTA-4 are used. In mines where methane is present, underground users are equipped with intrinsically safe (central battery) telephones of the type ATI-CB. These telephones can be connected to the general telephone exchanges only through intrinsically safe feeding bridges (IAUL) installed in the telephone exchange buildings.

The schematic diagram of an ATI-CB telephone and the principle of its operation in conjunction with a feeding bridge IAUL are presented in Fig. 5.1. An ATI-CB telephone is equipped with electro-acoustic converters of the type W-69, used in the microphones, earphone and transmitter of call-signals. Calling the subscriber (terminal) of an ATI-CB telephone (through the telephone exchange and the IAUL feeding bridge) is carried out using an alternating current of about 12 V and a frequency of 1150 Hz $\pm$ 50 Hz, modulated with the signal $f_m = 3$ Hz. This signal travels from the line into a calling insert (installed in the front of the telephone). This type of telephone has neither a polarized buzzer nor inductor.

In the new generation of telephones (types TK, TKA), designed for underground coal mines, the installation of a selector keyboard is planned: this will permit digital dialing according to the code-frequency system meeting the requirements of CCITT, or decimal pulse dialing. Moreover, these telephones make it possible to call the mine dispatch office for normal, automatic (time system) and alarm procedures, and to transmit alarm warnings given by mine dispatcher (TKA).

Thus these telephones can take over the functions of the general dispatching loudspeaking systems of the AUD type. The rated level of usable signals in underground branch lines is 0 dB (0.775 V) and the frequency band of a code-frequency dialing system is from 688 Hz to

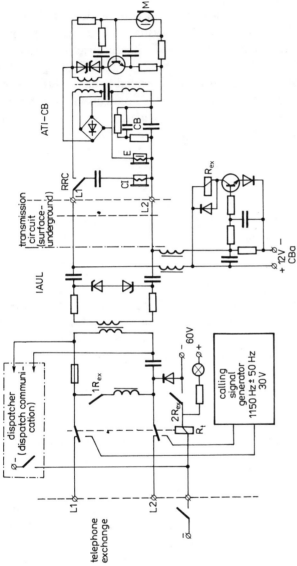

Fig. 5.1 Simplified schematic diagram of an intrinsically safe telephone set (ATI-CB) operating with a feeding bridge (IAUL); M—microphone, E—earphone, CI—calling insert, CB—line balance, RRC—reed relay connector, R_{ex}—exchange call relay, R_t—telephone set call relay, CBa—central battery for intrinsically safe telephones

1000 Hz (at on output level of 6 dB) and from 1000 to 1496 Hz (at output level of 3 dB) [33].

The *local communication system* is used exclusively for communication in a limited area, with no possibility of communication with the terminals of the other communication systems. This type of communication serves those work stations which are strictly related to a common production task, isolated technological lines, etc. In local communications, telephones are usually connected in parallel to a common line (with no switchboard) or in a star connection to a central switchboard, located at a dispatch point. In methane-rich mines, local communication systems use intrinsically safe ATG type telephones. These are local battery telephones (usually of the R-20) with a magneto-type calling system (a multi-pole magneto). The frequency of a magneto calling signal at 180 rev/min is 1000 Hz. Conversion of the electric calling signal into an acoustic signal takes place in the earphone of the handset and in a spare earphone. In these telephones, electrodynamic converters of the type W-69 are used both as microphone and as earphone (double action converters).

In *dispatch communication networks* special low capacity (from 80 to 40 users) switchboards, operated manually by the dispatcher, are used. In principle, such a switchboard is not used for communication between the users (terminals) but for two-way communication (user-dispatcher) only. As a rule, in dispatch communications, telephones of the KTA or ATI-CB type are used. The possibility of holding so-called conference talks is a characteristic feature of a dispatch communication network. Connecting the switchboard with an underground user may be carried out directly or by using the general (all-mine) telephone circuits of underground users (parallel and dispatch-user circuits); the dispatcher may, at any time, communicate with an underground user, even terminating his connection with the telephone exchange.

5.1.2 Radiotelephone communication

Radiotelephone communication is, first of all, used in underground transport—in both trolley and battery-driven electric traction systems. Most often, long-wave radiotelephones are used: TRG-1k in trolley traction (so-called trolley-phones) and TRGI in battery-driven electric traction. There are two types of TRGI radiotelephones: TRGI-1R designed for operation with a frame antenna and a locomotive, and the

TRGI-1P which operates with a loop antenna (for the transport dispatcher). The TRG-1k and TRGI-1 radiotelephones operate as frequency modulation systems. Their structural diagram is presented in Fig. 5.2 and their basic specifications in Table 5.1.

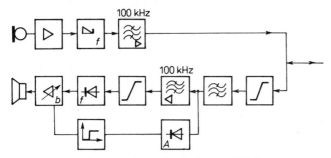

Fig. 5.2 Block diagram of a radiotelephone of TRG type

TABLE 5.1   Electric parameters of mining radiotelephones of the TRG-1k and TRGI types

Quantity	Unit	TRG-1k	TRGI
Transmitter			
Operation frequency	kHz	100	100
Frequency stability	kHz	$\pm 1 \times 10^{-2}$	$\pm 5 \times 10^{-2}$
Frequency deviation	kHz	± 3	± 2
Output power	W	10	0.8
Output resistance	Ω	40	5000(TRGI-1R)
			600(TRGI-1P)
Receiver			
Sensitivity	μV		387
Noise suppression threshold	mV	3–30	2.45
Received modulated signal band-width	kHz		4.8
Frequency bandwidth of l.f. circuit	Hz	600–3200	
Output power	W	5	0.6
Supply voltage	V	12 (locomotive battery)	12(ZRI-6Ah)
Current consumption			
(a) during reception	A	0.2–1	0.2
(b) during transmission	A	3	0.25

A mine communication system comprising, in the most general sense of the word, the transmission of information (e.g. speech, conventional signals, digital data, measurement values and control signals) consists also of other systems, commonly called dispatch systems, and most important [18, 20], systems of monitoring safety parameters (mainly mine atmosphere and crump hazards) and technological parameters. A characteristic feature of these systems is the use of separate dispatch-switchboard units (exchanges) and the possibility to use common teletransmission lines (dispatch lines) incorporated in a single cable together with telephone lines. Of the systems used in mines, which at least partially make use of these common telecommunication lines, we can for example mention the following:

— methane detection (periodical CH_4 measurement, e.g. CMC-1 systems) and demethanization control,
— monitoring the physical parameters of mine atmosphere and ventilation control,
— monitoring the production parameters (mining, horizontal and vertical transport, operating of other devices),
— technological communications for work-faces and transport routes.

Other telecommunication lines are used for example in the systems of radio control of machines and the monitoring of staff movement, and especially in the system for locating tremors—monitoring and forecasting crump (rock-fall) hazards (monitoring of rock movements), where seismo-acoustic and microseismic methods, and small-diameter drill-holes are used.

5.2   Wire teletransmission lines—types of cables used and principal parameters

In mines, symmetrical cable lines (circuits) are used for the transmission (teletransmission) of information, e.g. speech, and control and monitoring signals. The basic elements of mine telecommunication lines (sets of circuits) consist of telecommunication cables and equipment such as cubicles and distribution boxes as well as cable boxes and terminals.

Modern mining telecommunication cables (e.g. the Polish types YTKGXFody, YTKGXFty) are usually built of single-wire copper cores with a diameter of 0.8 mm in polyethylene or PVC insulation, laid in pairs, quads or star quads. Armoured (e.g. YKSYFty, YKSGFo) and unarmoured (YKSY) signal cables are also used in low-voltage power, monitoring, control and safety circuits. Telephone signalling cables (e.g. YSTKGXFty, YSTKGXFoy) are used primarily in shaft signalling circuits. Examples of the typical structure of cables of these types are presented in Figs. 5.3 and 5.4.

The proper operation of cable circuits depends to a great extent on correct values of parameters determining the required quality of

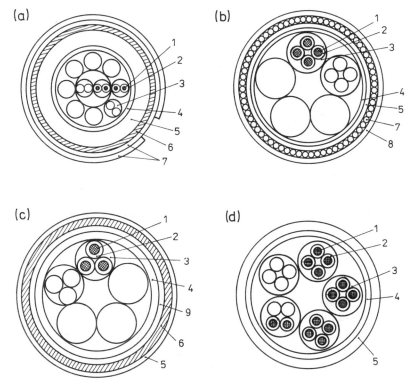

Fig. 5.3 Principle of construction of mining telephone cables: (a) paired cable of the TKGFt type (10 × 2 × 0.8 mm), (b) quadded cable of the YTKGXFoy type (5 × 4 × 0.8 mm, (c) triple, station, screened cable of the YTKGYekw type (5 × 3 × 0.5 mm), (d) quadded cable with steel-copper cores of the YTKGMFLY type (5 × 4 × 0.5 mm²); 1—cores, 2—core insulation, 3—cable quad, 4—wrapping, 5—sheath, 6—fibre wrapping, 7—armouring, 8—anticorrosive tube, 9—screen (foil wrapping and earthed wire)

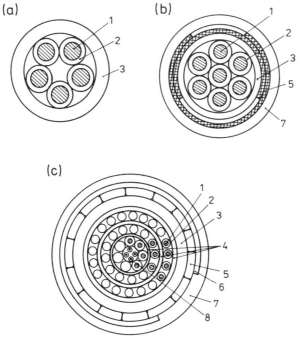

Fig. 5.4 Principle of construction of mining cables: signalling cables (a, b) and signalling
       telephone cables (c); (a) of the YKSY type (5×2.5 mm^2), (b) of the YKSYFty type
       (7×1.5 mm^2), (c) of the YSTKGXFpdy type (4×0.8 mm $+ 40 \times 2.5$ mm^2);
       1—core, 2—core insulation, 3—sheath, 4—insulative wrapping, 5—armouring,
       6—reverse spiral casing, 7—anticorrosive tube, 8—telephone pairs

transmission. As for every electrical circuit (line), these include first of all
specific electric parameters (per unit length): the longitudinal parameters
(resistance R and inductance L), and the transverse ones (capacity C and
leakage G) (Fig. 5.5), and moreover wave parameters such as the
impedance Z_w, the attenuation constant α and the phase constant β. In
a general case, the wave impedance is expressed by the formula

$$Z_w = \sqrt{\frac{R+j\omega L}{G+j\omega C}} \, . \tag{5.1}$$

For high-frequencies $\omega L \gg R$ and $G \ll \omega C$, and therefore the
so-called nominal wave (characteristic) impedance of a circuit [26] is
expressed by the formula

$$Z_w = \sqrt{\frac{L}{C}} \, . \tag{5.2}$$

Fig. 5.5 Substitute diagram for a teletransmission circuit

The values of Z_w, α and β are determined from the measurements of input impedance of a circuit with the length l in the short-circuited state (Z_{sc}) and in the no-load (open) state (Z_0), from the equation

$$Z_w = \sqrt{Z_{sc} Z_0} = \sqrt{|Z_{sc}||Z_o|} \, e^{j\frac{\varphi_{sc}+\varphi_0}{2}}, \tag{5.3}$$

$$\tanh(A+jB) = \sqrt{\frac{Z_{sc}}{Z_0}} = S e^{j\varphi_s}, \tag{5.4}$$

where

$$S = \left| \sqrt{\frac{Z_{sc}}{Z_0}} \right|, \quad \varphi_s = \arg \sqrt{\frac{Z_{sc}}{Z_0}}$$

and, after transformation

$$A = l\alpha = \frac{1}{2} \operatorname{arctanh}\left(\frac{2S}{2+S^2} \cos\varphi_s\right), \tag{5.5}$$

$$B = l\beta = \frac{1}{2} \operatorname{arctanh}\left(\frac{2S}{1-S^2} \sin\varphi_s + k\pi\right), \tag{5.6}$$

where $k = 1, 2, 3, \ldots$

The wave attenuation A is defined for a circuit operating in the condition of impedance matching on the reception side. In practice, this condition is only seldom met. Therefore, use is made of the notion of the effective attenuation A_{ef}, determined for the true conditions of circuit supply and loading, which is expressed by the formula

$$A_{ef} = 10 \log \frac{P_1}{P_2}, \tag{5.7}$$

where

P_1 — the power, which can be given by a source with internal
impedance Z_a to a receiver with its impedance matched to this
source,

P_2 — the power, which is produced on the load connected to the
source by the circuit.

The effective attenuation determined for $Z_a = Z_b = 600\ \Omega$ is called the
overall loss A_o. It is generally measured under operating conditions.

In the practical evaluation of the suitability of a telecommunication
cable the following values are important: the electric strength (usually
500 or 750 V, 50 Hz or 1200 V DC), the core and its insulation
resistances, the effective capacity between cores constituting a pair, the
resistance asymmetry and the capacitance asymmetry. And thus for
example resistane of the cores of telecommunication mining cables (at
20°C) should not exceed [27]: 37 $\Omega \cdot \mathrm{km}^{-1}$ for telephone cables with
a core diameter of 0.8 mm and 13 $\Omega \cdot \mathrm{km}^{-1}$ for signal cables with a core
cross-sectional area of 1.5 mm²; whereas the insulation resistance should
not be lower than 5000 $\mathrm{M\Omega \cdot km}$ in polyethylene cables and 20 $\mathrm{M\Omega \cdot km}$ in
PVC cables. The permissible value of the effective capacity of a pair of
cores is 60 $\mathrm{nF \cdot km}^{-1}$ in polyethylene-insulated cables and 120 $\mathrm{nF \cdot km}^{-1}$
in PVC-insulated cables. More specific data concerning the basic

TABLE 5.2   Elementary and wave parameters of telecommunication quadded mining
cables of the types YTKGX ($n \times 4 \times 0.8$ mm)

f	R	L	G	C	Z_w	α	β
[kHz]	[Ω/km]	[mH/km]	[mS/km]	[nF/km]	[Ω]	[dB/km]	[rad/km]
0.1	68.41	0.72	0.0021	49.51	1481	0.292	0.0316
0.2	68.43	0.72	0.0023	49.50	1048	0.405	0.0455
0.5	68.48	0.72	0.0029	49.49	663	0.629	0.0735
1.0	68.40	0.72	0.0032	49.48	469	0.868	0.1063
2.0	68.83	0.71	0.0058	49.44	334	1.196	0.1554
3.0	68.77	0.71	0.0072	49.41	274	1.412	0.1971
5.0	69.23	0.71	0.020	49.52	216	1.734	0.2708
7.0	69.76	0.70	0.040	49.36	187	1.928	0.3415
10	71.29	0.70	0.056	49.81	163	2.200	0.4453
20	78.49	0.69	0.106	50.22	136	2.732	0.8022
50	94.38	0.68	0.294	51.54	120	3.634	1.9018
80	106.88	0.64	0.490	49.48	116	4.031	2.9471

parameters of quadded mining cables can be found in Table 5.2 [32], whereas Table 5.3 gives examples of requirements for non-coil-loaded cable circuits in branch networks for $f = 800$ Hz [75].

TABLE 5.3   Attenuation constant α [dB/km] and elementary resistance of the loop R [Ω/km] of non-coil-loaded cable circuits with core diameter d [mm]

d [mm]	α — for effective capacity of a cable		R [Ω/km]
	40 nF/km	50 nF/km	
0.5	1.20	1.34	190
0.6	1.00	1.12	132
0.8	0.74	0.83	74

5.3   Circuit resistance and its asymmetry, and cable circuit insulation resistance

5.3.1   Circuit resistance

The upper limit of allowable resistance of a subscriber (branch) circuit (loop), when disconnected from the telephone and short-circuited at the end, depends on the type of exchange (or other device) with which the telecommunication circuit operates. For the types of telephone exchange used in mines, the greatest permissible value of loop resistance is between 1000 and 1700 Ω. The unreliable operation of communication systems, even when using intrinsically safe sets (of the ATI-CB type), caused by too high a resistance of the circuit loop, occurs frequently in mines. Considering that telecommunication lines in mines may be some 10–15 km long, the resistance of the loop (in case of a 0.8 mm core diameter) may substantially exceed 1000 Ω, since in practice, the relatively high values of the additional connection resistance at the points where cables are joined (in cable boxes, joints and cubicles) should also be taken into account. In some mines two pairs of cables are used as a single circuit line of a telecommunication cable as a prevention. Test measurements of the resistance of mine circuit were carried out using digital multimeters of the V-543 and VC-10T types. For each circuit (loop) the value of the resistance was measured twice, reversing the direction of the measurement current.

TABLE 5.4   Relative division of the results of measurements of the resistance of insulation R_i of mining subscribers lines

Mines denotation	Number of lines examined	Percentage of the results of measurements within the ranges:															
		> 95 MΩ	95– > 85 MΩ	85– > 75 MΩ	75– > 65 MΩ	65– > 55 MΩ	55– > 45 MΩ	45– > 35 MΩ	35– > 25 MΩ	25– > 15 MΩ	15– > 5 MΩ	5– > 2.5 MΩ	2.5– > 1 MΩ	1– > 0.5 MΩ	0.5– > 0.1 MΩ	≤ 0.1 MΩ	≤ 5 MΩ
KWK 1	734	4.9	1.4	1.0	1.6	2.3	3.4	7.5	8.3	18.3	20.3	6.5	6.3	5.2	8.6	4	30.5
KWK 2	280	8.6	1.4	1.4	1.1	7.9	4.6	8.9	11.1	12.5	14.3	4.6	10.4	3.6	7.9	1.8	28.2
KWK 3	154	23.4	0.0	2.0	2.0	1.0	4.0	1.3	5.8	2.6	8.4	6.5	14.3	9.7	11.7	7.8	50.6
KWK 4	298	23.2	1.7	0.7	1.3	1.7	2.0	4.4	5.4	6.0	16.4	12.8	10.1	4.7	7.4	2.3	37.2
KWK 5	248	15.7	2.0	1.2	2.0	0.4	2.8	2.8	3.6	6.0	14.1	4.4	5.2	8.5	18.5	12.5	49.2
KWK 6	209	13.4	0.0	1.9	1.0	1.9	12.9	7.2	8.1	15.8	22.0	4.8	5.3	1.4	4.3	0.0	15.8
KWK 7	188	1.6	0.0	1.1	0.5	2.1	3.2	3.7	4.8	14.4	39.4	9.6	10.6	4.3	3.7	1.1	29.3
Total	2111	12.9	0.9	1.4	1.4	2.5	4.7	5.1	6.7	10.8	19.3	7.0	8.9	5.3	8.8	4.2	34.2

   Auxiliary circuits were used in measuring resistance asymmetry. The
measured values for the asymmetry of cable circuits of various lengths
fall within the following limits: 0–5 Ω in circuits 8 km long, 0.3–4.4 Ω in
circuits 7 km long, and 0.5–3 Ω in circuits 3.6–4.4 km long; in one circuit,
in which one telephone core was made up of a number of wire groups, the
asymmetry was 162 Ω.
   In circuits of long-distance telecommunication systems, the asymmetry of cores belonging to the same group should not exceed 2 Ω for a core
diameter exceeding 1 mm, and 3 Ω for cores of smaller diameter (for
multiple communication circuits the permissible asymmetry is even
lower) [76].

5.3.2   Circuit insulation resistance

The resistance of one core of a branch circuit (cable, equipment, set)
against another core connected to earth should be at least 5 MΩ [75].
A summary of the results of measurements carried out in underground
networks of seven underground coal mines are given in Table 5.4 and 5.5.
   These measurements were carried out using an intrinsically safe meter
of the IMC-type with a measurement range from 10 kΩ to 100 MΩ.
Measurements were taken in telephone exchanges (in an underground
distribution frame at the surface of a mine) and at linear terminals of

TABLE 5.5   Mean values of the resistance of insulation R_i of subscribers lines in underground coal mines

Mine denota-tion KWK	Number of lines examined n	Mean value $\bar{R}_i = \dfrac{\Sigma R_i}{n}$ [MΩ]	Variances [MΩ²]	Standard deviation [MΩ]	Notes
1	734	22.0	700	26.4	It has been assumed in
2	278	30.2	935	30.6	the calculations that
3	154	32.8	1706	41.3	the resistance values
4	298	35.0	1572	39.6	which exceed the
5	248	26.7	1407	37.5	range of the measure-
6	209	34.5	1033	32.1	ment scale of the me-
7	188	15.6	363	18.2	ter (0.01–100 MΩ) is equal to 10 kΩ or 100 MΩ respectively
Total	2111	26.9	1052	32.4	

branch (subscriber) circuits for each core of a pair switched off subsequently (the other core was earthed). An analysis of the measurements shows that the resistance of the insulation of 30 to 50% of the circuits examined is lower than 5 MΩ; in practice values above 95 MΩ were found to occur in only "short" circuits such as in the case of sets installed in headings close to shafts.

The resultant value of the circuit insulation resistance R_i depends not only on the length l_c and on the insulation resistance per unit length R_{ic} of the cable, but, to a great extent, also on the number n_p of connections and terminals (e.g. contact bolts and terminal in cables headings and boxes) and the condition of their insulation R_{ip}, i.e.

$$R_i = \frac{1}{\dfrac{l_c}{R_{ic}} + \dfrac{n_p}{R_{ip}}} . \tag{5.8}$$

5.4   Attenuation and capacity asymmetry of a circuit

5.4.1   Effective attenuation of a circuit

For a local cable network, the overall permissible loss, measured for the frequency of 800 Hz [75] is laid down in standards. For example it is 4.34 dB (0.5 Np), for a subscriber (branch) line 30.4 dB (3.5 Np) for a chain of links, and 0.87–1 dB (0.1 Np) for passage through the exchange. In plant telecommunication networks, the overall loss between the exchange and the terminal should not exceed 4.34 dB [77].

The results of measurements of the effective attenuation carried out for networks in several underground coal mines in the system as presented in Fig. 5.6, are given in Fig. 5.7. For frequencies up to 10 kHz, $Z_a = Z_b = 600$ Ω was assumed, whereas for $f > 10$ kHz the values $Z_a = Z_b = 150$ Ω were used. The results of the measurements of the wave impedance Z_w, the attenuation constant α and the wave phase shift

Fig. 5.6 Principle of measuring the effective attenuation

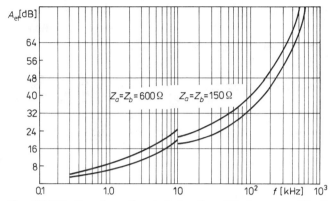

Fig. 5.7 Effective attenuation A_{ef} in function of the frequency f (for the example of mining circuits with a length of 7.7–8.1 km)

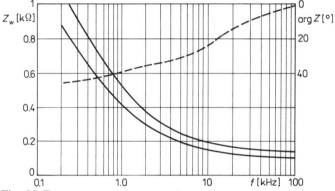

Fig. 5.8 Frequency characteristics of the wave impedance (modulus and argument) of mine cable telephone circuits

constant β are presented in Figs. 5.8 and 5.9 as a function of frequency. The values were calculated (using formulas (5.3)–(5.6)) from measurements of Z_{sc} and Z_0 carried out in mine networks using a Grützmacher bridge of the type E-304M with direct modulus and φ angle readings. For the purpose of comparison, the broken line in Fig. 5.9 marks the α and β values for a quadded telecommunication cable of the YTKGX type [32].

5.4.2   Cross-talk attenuation

Couplings and coupling asymmetries of circuits are the cause of signal cross-talk between the circuits of telecommunication lines. Within the range of acoustic frequencies, the level of cross-talk is determined by the capacitive asymmetry, however, with increasing frequency, the influence of the asymmetry of mutual inductances becomes increasingly important; for frequencies of 20–25 kHz the influence of the asymmetry of mutual inductance is, approximately, the same as that of the capacitive asymmetry [4]. The cross-talk induced by the asymmetry of mutual resistance of the circuits equals 20–40% of that due to the asymmetry of mutual inductances, whereas the cross-talk caused by the asymmetry of circuit leakage is 10–15% of the cross-talk resulting from capacitive asymmetry [4]. The phenomenon of cross-talk is expressed through the

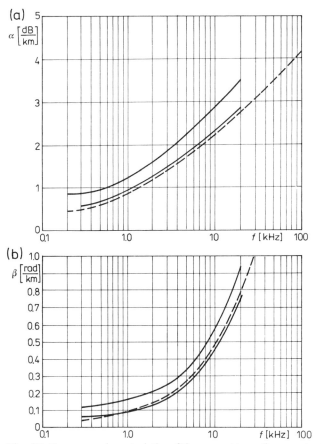

Fig. 5.9 Frequency characteristics of the wave attenuation constant α and the phase shift constant β of mine telecommunication circuits

notion of the cross-talk attenuation A_z defined as the logarythmic ratio
of the apparent power of the signal transmitted in the interfering cable
circuit P_1, to the apparent power of the signal P_2 received (due to
cross-talk) in the receiver connected to the interfered cable circuit (both
circuits operate in the condition of impedance matching):

$$A_z = 10\log\frac{P_1}{P_2}. \tag{5.9}$$

Depending on the path followed by the interfering signal from the source
in the interfering circuit to the receiver in the circuit being interfered
with, we distinguish a "near-end" attenuation A_{ne} and a "far-end"
attenuation A_{fe}.

Measurements of near-end attenuation were carried out using
a generator with a symmetric output and with a selective level meter, for
a manufacturer's length (about 300 m) of the YTKGXFty ($33 \times 2 \times 0.8$
mm) cable. The A_{ne} values calculated from the results of the measurements for a range of frequencies are shown in Fig. 5.10: the broken line
marks the range and mean value of near-end attenuation for quadded

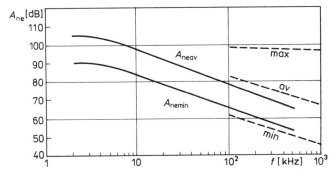

Fig. 5.10 Frequency characteristics of the near-end attenuation A_{ne} of a manufacturer's
length of a paired telephone cable of the YTKGXFty type ($33 \times 2 \times 0.8$ mm)
(continuous lines)

mining cable, as given by the manufacturer. On the other hand, the
results of the measurements (range and mean values) of near-end
attenuation, carried out in telephone networks of several underground
coal mines, are presented in Fig. 5.11.

Between the near-end attenuation for the manufacturer's length of cable of length n, and the attenuation for a length l, there exists a relationship

$$A_{nel} = A_{nen} + 20\log\sqrt{4n\alpha} - 20\log\sqrt{1-e^{-4l\alpha}} \qquad [\text{dB}], \qquad (5.10)$$

where α is the attenuation constant (expressed in Np). Low values of near-end attenuations measured in mines (Fig. 5.11) indicate cable

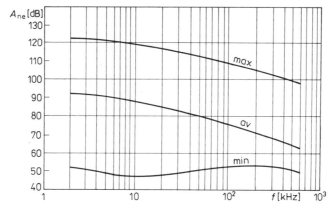

Fig. 5.11 The range of variation near-end attenuation A_{ne} of mine telecommunication
circuits

damage or wire change-over (i.e. pairs of cores belonging to different quads). An example of the influence of wire change-over A_{ne} is presented in Fig. 5.12. For a piece of YTKGXFty cable ($24 \times 2 \times 0.8$ mm) with a length of 100 m, the measurements of near-end attenuation were carried out under the following conditions: 1—attenuation between pair 1 (cores 1a and 1b) and pair 2 (2a and 2b), 2—attenuation between the pairs made up of the cores 1a and 2a and 1b and 2b, 3—attenuation between the pair made of the cores 1a and 2a and the pair 3 (3a and 3b), 4—attenuation between the pairs 1 and 2 (core 1a earthed).

Cross-talk between earthed pairs were measured to investigate the influence of introducing by-passes for trolleyphone communication in telephone cables. The results of the measurements prove that a wire change-over or the earthing of one core causes a substantial reduction of near-end attenuation.

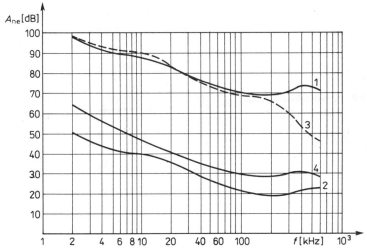

Fig. 5.12 Results of near-end attenuation A_{ne} measurements in a YTKGXFty (24 × 2 × 0.8 mm) cable: 1—cross-talk between the pairs 1 (cores 1a and 1b) and 2 (cores 2a and 2b); 2—attenuation between pairs made of cores 1a and 2a and of cores 1b and 2b; 3—cross-talk between the pair made of cores 1a and 2a and the pair 3 (3a and 3b); 4—cross-talk between the pairs 1 and 2 in case where a core of one of the pairs is earthed

The cross-talk interval ΔA_z, for a cable telephone lines is defined as

$$\Delta A_z = A_{fe} - A_w, \tag{5.11}$$

where

A_{fe} —far-end attenuation,
A_w —wave attenuation of a link (junction).

The cross-talk interval between two circuits in the main network inter-cubicle, etc. cables, should not be lower than 65 dB (7.5 Np) [75].

5.4.3   Asymmetry of circuit capacity

Capacitive asymmetries of the k-type (from k_1 to k_{12}) [26], i.e. asymmetries between individual side circuits and phantom circuits of the same or different quads are differentiated, from asymmetries of the e-type (e_1-e_3), i.e. circuit capacity asymmetries relative to earth. Within the range of acoustic frequencies, k-type asymmetries are decisive as far as cross-talk phenomena in circuits are concerned, whereas the e-type asymmetries influence the susceptibility of a circuit to the inductive interaction of traction networks.

During the practical difficulties the measurements of earth-return asymmetry (input earth-return impedance) of telecommunication circuit in mine headings were carried out by a simplified method, whose principle is presented in Fig. 5.13. It has been assumed that for low frequencies and relatively short circuits, the "observable" impedance between the input terminals of the circuit and the earth is of a capacitive nature (Fig. 5.13b). Therefore we can write (Fig. 5.13b):

$$U = -2j\omega ER\,\Delta C. \tag{5.12}$$

If we express the E to U ratio in dB (a_c) and assume $R = 300\ \Omega$ we obtain

$$a_c = 20\log\frac{E}{U}, \tag{5.13}$$

$$\Delta C = \frac{1}{600\omega\cdot 10^{(a_c/20)}}. \tag{5.14}$$

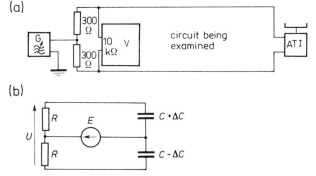

Fig. 5.13 System for the indirect measurement of the asymmetry of the impedance (capacity) relative to earth of a circuit (a), and its substitute diagram (b)

In reality, the results of the measurements are also influenced by the circuit resistance and leakage asymmetries. The a_c versus frequency characteristics $a_c(\omega)$ has a number of extremes. To allow a comparison of results, the asymmetry measurements were carried out at a constant frequency. The investigations were conducted in several mines (200 randomly selected circuits of various lengths), and the results are presented in the form of a histogram in Fig. 5.14, while the frequency characteristics are shown in Fig. 5.15. Figure 5.14 reveals that over 65% of the circuits which were examined are characterized by an asymmetry of over 50 dB. The values in Fig. 5.15 do not agree with equation (5.14), and the reason for this probably lies in the R and L asymmetry of the circuits and the wave effect in the earth circuit (correspondence occurs only for low frequencies and circuit lengths up to 100 metres).

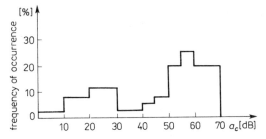

Fig. 5.14 Histogram of the asymmetry of the input impedance relative to earth of mine circuits being examined

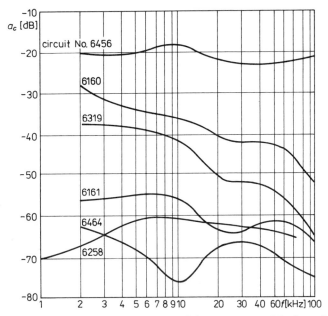

Fig. 5.15 Frequency characteristics of the asymmetry of the input impedance a_c of mine telephone circuits (example of 6 circuits in KWK 1)

5.5 Psophometric voltages and their measurement in underground telephone networks and some requirements

The quality of speech transmission mostly depends on the quality of telephone transmission, which is evaluated on the basis of a statistical investigation of logatom articulation, and, through this, the intelligibility of speech. Under operating conditions, the quality of telephone communication may be evaluated by determining the psophometric voltage (power) of noise (interference) measured at a particular junction of the circuit (at the terminals of either a set or a telephone exchange).

By the psophometric voltage of interference U_p we understand the r.m.s. voltage value at a reference frequency f_0, which, if it were to occur in a telecommunication circuit instead of a real interference voltage, causes an identical reduction of telephone transmission quality as the real interference. The psophometric voltage is expressed by the formula

$$U_p = \sqrt{\sum (p_f U_f)^2}\,, \tag{5.15}$$

where

U_f — r.m.s. value of the interference voltage occurring in a telephone circuit at the frequency f,

p_f — psophometric weight coefficient at the frequency f.

The reference frequency f_0, against which the evaluation of the harmful effect of interference voltages at different frequencies is carried out, is specified to be 800 Hz for telephone transmission and 1000 Hz for line broadcasting transmission. The influence of interference voltages at different frequencies upon the quality of telephone transmission is accounted for by the psophometric weight coefficient p_f, using which we evaluate the extent to which an earphone (or human ear) is more (or less) sensitive to the interference voltage U_f at the given frequency f than to the voltage U_0 at the reference frequency f_0; this coefficient is expressed by the formula

$$p_f = \frac{U_0}{U_f}, \tag{5.16}$$

with the assumption that both voltages are equivalent to each other with respect to the induced interference effect. The variation of the telephone T and radio R psophometric weight coefficients as a function of frequency is illustrated in Fig. 5.16.

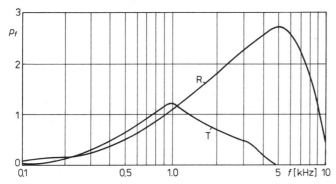

Fig. 5.16 Psophometric weight coefficients p_f in function of the frequency f

The psophometric electromotive force has been defined as double the value of the psophometric voltage of interference measured across a resistance of 600 Ω. In the standards regulating mine telephone networks there are no specifications concerning the permissible values of voltages, electromotive force and psophometric power, nor the methods of interference measurement. There are also no measuring apparatuses appropriate to the specific environmental conditions of mines, particularly of methane-rich mines. Therefore, the measurements concerning interference in underground telecommunication networks were carried out on the surface, in an underground distribution frame of a telephone exchange.

Diagrams of the measuring systems are presented in Fig. 5.17: (a) the system for measuring and recording the "unweighted" level U (broadband) and the psophometric level U_p; (b) the system for measuring and recording the level of selective interference. The voltage was measured with a selective nanovoltmeter (UNIPAN-223) and recorded across a load impedance of 600 Ω (psophometer input impedance), with simultaneous monitoring (oscilloscope) and listening in (telephone earphone). To take into account the unsymmetrical input of a selective meter, a psophometer (in the configuration for broad-band measurements) was introduced between the circuit and the selective meter. This psophometer functions as a symmetrizing device, as a rated load of the circuit (impedance of 600 Ω) and as a preamplifier, and also makes it possible to simultaneousy record the broad-band level of the interference voltage.

As has already been mentioned, the absence of standardized specifications for permissible levels of interference in mine telephone
networks makes it difficult to objectively assess the true significance of
the measurements carried out. Such specifications do, however, exist for
general-use telephone networks.

In general, the level of the mean-power psophometric noise in an
subscriber's line (the level of the psophometric voltage measured with the
impedance of 600 Ω) should not exceed -63 dB, i.e. 548 μV (i.e. it should
not exceed 500 pW). This voltage level is determined on the basis of
measuring the mean value over a 1-minute interval. The specifications
concerning the mean power of psophometric noise do not differentiate as
to the source of this interference, as meeting these requirements ensures
a good quality of telephone communication. It is assumed, however, that
the principal sources of interference are power and traction lines;
therefore, the permissible levels of interference voltage, resulting from
the coupling of a communication circuit with these lines, are determined
separately. The CCITT recommendations specify the permissible psophometric electromitive force of a noise induced as a result of

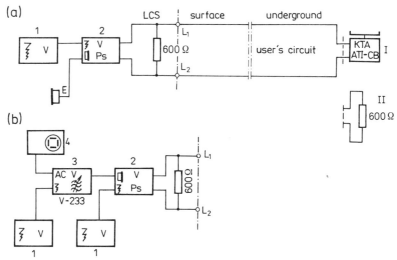

Fig. 5.17 Principle of voltage measurement: (a) psophometric or unweighted, (b) selective
with simultaneous record of unweighted voltage level—in a subscriber's circuit
loaded with a telephone set (KTA, ATI) or with substitute resistance of 600 Ω:
1—recording voltmeter, 2—voltmeter with a psophometric filter, 3—selective
voltmeter, 4—oscilloscope, LCS—line control socket

electromagnetic couplings with all the power lines interacting with one or more parts of a set of telephone links connecting the user's set with the exchange. This should not exceed 1 mV at the terminals of the set (when one is listening) providing that the "telecommunication devices connected with set are balanced against earth as well as it is possible, using the most up-to-date version of the device".

The specified value of the psophometric interference voltage depends on the rated value of a usable signal (transmission level), and thus the level of 1 mV of interferences refers to the level of a usable signal, namely -0.8 Np $(-7$ dB). Regulations [82] determine what conversion factors are to be used for other levels of usable signals. For cable telephone lines of the Polish railways, the specified values of the electromotive force of psophometric interference may not exceed 1.4 mV; whereas in isolated networks (not connected directly with the public telephone system) in Federal Republic of Germany [28], the value of the psophometric force is allowed to reach 5 mV.

The highest values of the psophometric interferences voltage, measured with a resistance of 600 Ω in the underground telephone networks of several mines, ranged from -40 dB to -50 dB. Table 5.6 gives examples of the values of the psophometric interference voltage measured in three mines. The value of the psophometric interference voltage is influenced primarily, by the presence or absence of an electric wire traction system.

TABLE 5.6 Example of the percentage division of the results of the measurements of psophometric interference voltages

Mine denotation	Number of underground telephone sets	Number of lines examined	> -75 dB	-75 to -70 dB	< -70 dB	Notes
KWK 6	200	43	76.7%	14%	9.3%	Methane-rich mine, ATI-CB
KWK 8	200	37	75.7%	8.1%	16.2%	Non-methane mine, KTA
KWK 9	400	190	72.6%	13.7%	13.7%	Methane-rich mine, ATI-CB

There are no standards for the mean power of unweighted noise nor the level of selective interference. It is assumed that the permissible level of selective interference for low-frequency transmission channels, measured at the output for each frequency (50 Hz, 100 Hz, 200 Hz, 250 Hz, 300 Hz, etc.) separately, should not exceed -50 dB, while the total level of this interference should not exceed -43 dB.

5.6 Internal interference in telephone communication—cross-talk in call signals

The use of bi-directional electro-acoustic converters in local and general (all-mine) telephone sets (ATG, ATI-CB) influences the possibility of interference penetration of the telephone communication system used in methane-rich mines.

Interference measurements in the underground telecommunication circuits presented in the present section were carried out from the surface, with the underground circuit loaded with the ATI-CB telephone set calling circuit. The crucial element of this telephone circuit is a bi-directional electro-acoustic converter of the type W-69 (calling insert) which, under these conditions of measurement, introduces additional interference, distorting the results of the measurements.

To eliminate the influence of electro-acoustic converters connected to any teletransmission circuit upon the results of measurements, the Polish Standards recommend replacing them with an equivalent resistance. However, the technological and logistical difficulties (telephone sets are at various levels and areas of a mine; necessity to open the sets) as well as the large number of measurements carried out in each mine resulted in this replacement have been omitted. Therefore, this section presents selected results of the measurements of interference in circuits loaded with an ATI-CB telephone set located in chosen regions of a mine with particularly high noise levels.

For the proposed method of conducting the psophometric measurements in a mine network, one had to determine what the influence of the ATI-CB calling insert and of the earphone insert of the ATG sets upon the level of interference voltage measured at the linear terminals of a telephone exchange could be, as it should be noted that if these sets are located in headings with high noise levels of, the voltage measured at their linear terminals is the result of the conversion of the acoustic noise in the heading into a voltaic usable signal by the W-69 insert (standstill position—handset on the fork).

In local communication systems, a single ATG set located in a heading with a high level of noise makes speech between the remaining sets connected to the same circuit difficult. In the case of the ATI-CB sets, it is not possible to correctly determine the psophometric interference voltage in a telephone line terminated with this set through measurements carried out in a telephone exchange.

The influence of the acoustic noise of the space (heading) upon the value of the voltage induced at the terminals of the ATI-CB telephone set is presented in Figs. 5.18 and 5.19. In Fig. 5.18, the frequency characteristics of the calling circuit of an ATI-CB set with a W-69-2A insert, at a constant level of acoustic pressure $L_p = 90$ dB (relative to a zero level of acoustic pressure equal to 2×10^{-5} Pa), is presented; the sound with frequencies between 0.4 and 7 kHz was obtained from a sinusoidal generator supplying a column loudspeaker. Figure 5.19 presents the relationship between the voltage U at the set terminals and the acoustic noise L_p of the environment for a few frequencies.

The investigations proved [31] that mine headings, in which one could expect a substantial influence of noise upon the level of the interference voltage (as measured in a telephone line loaded with an intrinsically safe telephone set (ATI-CB, ATG)) include: (a) top roads

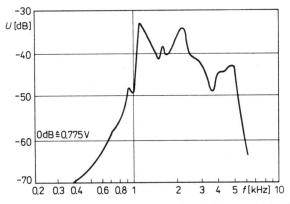

Fig. 5.18 Frequency characteristic of a telephone set of the ATI-CB type with a W-69-2A insert calling circuit ($L_p = 90$ dB)

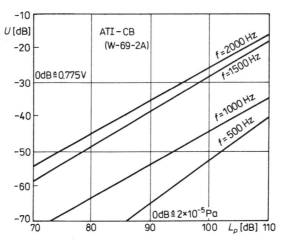

Fig. 5.19 The output voltage U of an ATI-CB set calling circuit as a function of the noise
intensity L_p with alternating frequency f

and bottom roads, (b) chutes, scraper gulleys and conveyor routes, (c)
compartments with compressors and main drainage pumps, (d) cross
headings close to ventilation fans, (e) cross-cuts and galleries where
locomotives operate. Accounting for the fact that the noise caused by
continuous operation of mining equipment is contained within the
frequency range up to 1000 Hz, the level of voltage measured at the
terminals of a telephone set ranges, as a rule, from -50 dB to -60 dB.
Examples of records of interference voltages in telephone lines terminated with ATI-CB sets (at the bottom of a skip shaft and in an air
roadway) are given in Fig. 5.20; the regularity of the peaks in Fig. 5.20a
results from the noise caused by the operation of loading gates, whereas
in Fig. 5.20b, the differences in the levels result from the noise caused by
the operation of mining machines at the working-face.

Another cause of internal interference (system interference) is the
cross-talk phenomenon, i.e. the partial permeation of a signal from its
proper track into the tracks of other signals, i.e. from one circuit into
another, in the same telephone line. In telephony, this permeation is
called cross-talk. Cross-talk is a typical phenomenon of multicircuit
lines, especially when individual circuits are close to one another. In
mine telecommunication networks, only linear cross-talk occurs as
a rule, i.e. cross-talk, as a result of which there occurs in the interfered
circuit an interference spectrum, whose components have only those

frequencies which were characteristic of the spectrum of the interfering signal. The main source of this type of interference in the telephone network of methane-rich mines is the cross-talk of the calling signal of ATI-CB sets. The strength of a calling signal, with a voltage of 12–15 V and a frequency of 1150 Hz ± 50 Hz modulated with a frequency of 3 Hz,

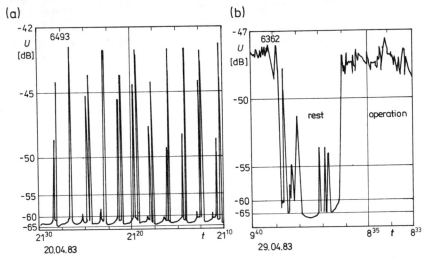

Fig. 5.20 Record of the interference voltage in a mine telephone circuit loaded with an ATI-CB set located: (b) at the bottom of the skip shaft, (b) in an air roadway

is too high for the environment operating conditions of a mine telecommunication network (low cross-talk attenuation). Examples of the influence of the ATI-CB set calling signal upon neighbouring circuits are presented in Fig. 5.21 in the form of records of interference voltages in a telephone circuit disconnected from the exchange, located in a multi-pair telecommunication cable, in which the neighbouring circuits were fed with a voltage from a calling signal generator of the type IAUL. The highest cross-talk voltages measured, caused by the IAUL calling signal, range from − 60 dB to − 40 dB. It should be stressed that the number of calls is generally less that twenty thousand in 24 hours (for the underground section of a telephone exchange only).

A substantial influence upon the propagation of the IAUL signal in both underground and surface networks of mines is exerted by the fact that mine telephone exchanges are not equipped for operation with

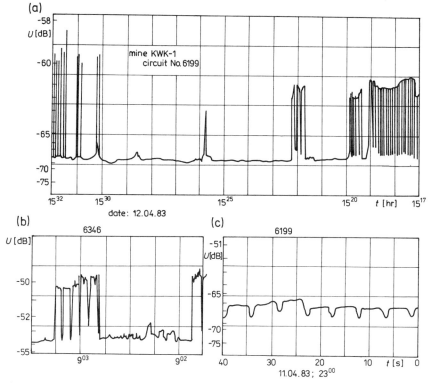

Fig. 5.21 Record of interference voltage in a mine telephone line induced by the cross-talk
of an ATI-CB set calling signal in the neighbouring circuits (for different record
speeds (a), (b), (c))

intrinsically safe telephone sets and with an IAUL feeding bridge.
A telephone exchange together with the IAUL elements is, therefore,
a substantial source of permeation of calling signal into other telephone
circuits.

5.7   The influence of dispatching alarm and warning systems on the level of the interference voltage in telecommunication lines

In underground coal mines the ALGUS and the more modern AUD-80
alarm systems are used. All the alarm systems have built-in systems
which monitor the continuity of circuits leading from the central mine

dispatch office to the signal boxes located in selected places in the headings. Teletransmission circuits, used in alarm systems, are incorporated in the same telecommunication cables as telephone communication circuits and with multiplex systems. In the ALGUS system, monitoring of core continuity is carried out with a 12–18 V AC current with a frequency of about 82 Hz, while the AUD-80 system uses 12–15 V AC and 25 Hz. A typical system contains about 80 ASA signal boxes located in haulage headings, shaft bottoms, and other important points of the underground mine, where staff may gather. As a rule, a separate pair of cores is guided to each signal box in a telecommunication cable. All the circuits are monitored with a 82 Hz voltage, taken from a single generating system. This system constitutes one of the sources of interference in underground telephone communications. The reason for this is the permeation of the basic 82 Hz frequency of the monitoring voltage (together with harmonics) into the telephone circuits.

More than 1000, randomly selected, mine telephone circuits in 7 mines having the ALGUS alarm system were investigated. Investigations were carried out for periods of 24 hours and for a week, and then repeated after intervals of a few-months and even after one-year intervals. The level of 1, 2 and 3 harmonic voltages was measured in the telephone circuits investigated. The measurements showed that daily fluctuations in the level of the cross-talk voltage of individual harmonics into telephone circuits is negligible. Such fluctuations are mainly related to the re-arrangement of the telecommunication and alarm networks, which takes place at intervals of a few days in air roadway and haulage headings and bottom and top roads. Another source of these fluctuations may be the deterioration of insulation condition, particularly at the ends of telecommunication lines which connect communication devices with telephone boxes; the most frequent cause of high interference values in the ALGUS system is wire changeover in the cable line. This is especially the case for steel-and-copper cables, which are often used in haulage bottom and in top roads on account of their higher mechanical resistance. In practice, this is one of the most important reasons for the low quality of communication with telephones located in bottom and top roads. The number of circuits investigated and of the values measured within the selected ranges of interference voltage at a frequency of 82 Hz in the underground telephone circuits is presented in Table 5.7.

TABLE 5.7   Relative division of the results of measurements of interference with the

Range of voltage values U_{82} [mV]	0–0.2	> 0.2–0.4	> 0.4–0.6	> 0.6–0.8	> 0.8–1	> 1.0–1.2	> 1.2–1.4
Number of investigated circuits	400	241	105	70	47	27	17
Percentage of circuits examined [%]	38.1	23	10	6.7	4.5	2.6	1.6

A more detailed analysis of the ALGUS system circuits with the highest level of interference revealed that these circuits (whose voltage U_{82} at a frequency of 82 Hz exceeded 2 mV) were characterized by very low insulation resistances by the earthing of one core, or by a significant asymmetry in insulation resistance. In the individual mines examined, the percentage of such circuits ranged from 5 to 15% (Table 5.8). These circuits were not included in the statistical analysis, the results of which are presented in the form of histograms in Fig. 5.22.

Examples of the results of the analysis of the interference voltage harmonics from the ALGUS system in selected telephone circuits from

TABLE 5.8   Statistical analysis of interference voltages with the frequency of 82 Hz

Mine denotation	Number of lines examined n	Percentage of lines where $U_{82} > 2mV$, [%]	Number of lines where $U_{82} \leqslant 2mV$ n_i	Mean value $\bar{U}_{82} = \dfrac{\Sigma U_{82}}{n_i}$ [μV]	Variance [μV²]	Standard deviation [μV]
KWK 1	361	15	306	408	198 000	445
KWK 2	140	9	128	333	137 000	370
KWK 6	230	5	219	283	78 000	280
KWK 7	94	6	88	318	90 000	300
KWK 9	225	13	196	508	198 000	445
Total	1050	11	937	381	158 000	398

frequency of 82 Hz (U_{82}) in the investigated telephone lines (KWK: 1, 2, 6, 7, 9)

> 1.4– 1.6	> 1.6– 1.8	> 1.8–2	> 2–3	> 3–5	> 5–10	> 10	Total
11	8	11	31	30	30	22	1050
1	0.8	1	3	2.9	2.9	2.1	100

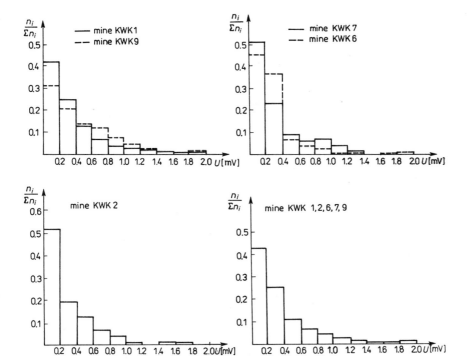

Fig. 5.22 Histograms of interference voltages with a frequency of 82 Hz in telephone lines (examples and mean values for five mines examined)

three mines are given in Table 5.9. It should be mentioned that the mine with the highest output and the most extensive telephone network (out of the five mines examined), whereas mine KWK 6 is a new mine in the process of being developed, and having only 40 ASA 1 signal boxes.

TABLE 5.9   Harmonics of interference voltages from the ALGUS system in mine telephone lines

Mine denotation	KWK 1			KWK 9			KWK 11			
f line no.	6199	6204	6418	6249	6261	6262	29	75	80	86
[Hz]	[mV]	[mV]	[mV]	[mV]	[mV]	[mV]	[mV]	[mV]	[mV]	[mV]
82	0.11	0.67	12.3	3.8	9.7	0.33	1.3	2.2	7.1	0.86
164	0.015	0.13	1.6	0.18	0.5	0.03	0.02	0.18	0.22	0.02
246	0.02	0.13	0.78	0.49	1.15	0.13	0.44	0.53	2.3	0.36
328		0.01		0.11	0.21	0.07	0.01			0.15
410					1.8		1.0			
U [dB]	−67	−57	−36	−45	−37	−65	−53	−58	−37	−47

It should also be mentioned that the quality of telephone communication is also influenced by the presence of other systems of monitoring and signalling as well as loudspeaking devices, whose circuits are located in telephone cables. This mostly applies to non-methane mines, where it is permitted to incorporate the circuits of telephone communication as well as other circuits in common telecommunication cables, providing their operating voltage does not exceed 120 V AC. As examples of such circuits the following can be mentioned: circuits for the measurement of shearer motor load, for the protection and illumination of drawing machines, and for loudspeaking devices.

5.8   The influence of an electric mine traction system on the level of interference in telephone lines

Electromagnetic interference generated by electric trolley (cable) traction systems exerts the greatest influence upon the telephone cable network in underground coal mines. This is primarily due to the fact that the spectrum of interference from an electric trolley traction system covers the entire frequency band of telephone communications including the range from 300 Hz up to 3400 Hz.

Measurements of interference due to traction systems in telephone circuits were carried out according to the diagrams presented in Fig. 5.17. Investigations were carried out in six mines equipped with electric trolley traction and ATI-CB and KTA telephone sets. Measurements of interference voltage levels (psophometric and unweighted) and the analysis of harmonics were carried out. On account of the high variability and the incidental nature of changes over very short periods of time, of individual harmonics generated by mine electric traction systems, it was decided to simultaneously record the voltage U and its harmonics (300 Hz, 600 Hz, 900 Hz). The 300 Hz harmonic covers the greatest part of the interference voltage spectrum. Recording time ranged from a few minutes to over 100 hours. A nanovoltmeter (UNIPAN-233) wit a "small" and "large" time constant was used for the measurements. An analysis of the results of the

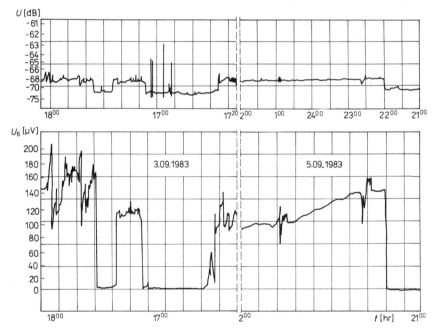

Fig. 5.23 Records of the interference voltage U and of the harmonic U_6 (300 Hz) in a mine telephone circuit (KWK 1); OdB $\hat{=}$ 0.775 V

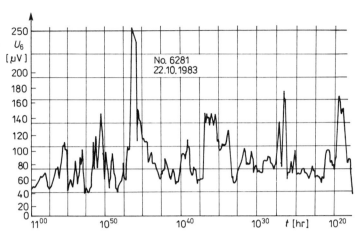

Fig. 5.24 Record of the interference voltage harmonic U_6 (300 Hz) in a telephone circuit
         (KWK 9)

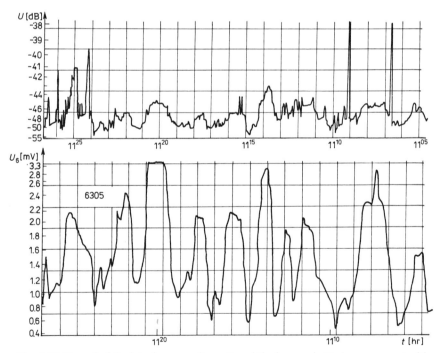

Fig. 5.25 Record of the interference voltage U and the harmonic U_6 (measurement with
          a detector with high (4 s) time constant) in a telephone circuit (KWK 10)

TABLE 5.10   Highest (U_{max}) and most frequently occurring (U_{av}) harmonic values of interference voltages in telephone lines caused by electric trolley traction systems

Underground coal mine (KWK)	Line no.	f [Hz]	U_{max} [mV]	U_{av} [mV]	Time of record [h]
1	6199	300	0.26	0.08–0.15	16
	6207	300	1.54	0.25–0.66	13
	6212	300	7	3–4	3
	6413	300	0.8	0.2–0.4	9
	6451	300	0.23	0.06–0.16	175
	6262	300	0.1	0.015–0.03	4.5
	6262	900	0.15	0.005–0.01	40
	6434	300	6	1–4	2
	6434	600	5	1.5–2.5	5.5
	6434	900	2.6	0.5–2.1	15.2
	6434	1500	1.5	0.9	0.5
	6311	1200	0.35	0.04–0.08	20
5	62	300	0.73	0.15–0.3	0.5
	93	300	0.27	0.05–0.15	0.5
	93	600	0.12	0.04–0.06	0.3
9	6136	300	1	0.2–0.4	1
	6269	300	0.75	0.1–0.5	0.5
	6281	300	0.4	0.06–0.12	2
	6438	300	0.31	0.06–0.2	2.5
10	6304	300	6.5	1–5	1
	6305	300	6.5	1–3	1
	6271	600	8	3–6	0.5

measurements reveals that in the course of a few minutes the changes in voltage level may reach a value of 30 dB. These changes do not take into account such states as e.g. switching off the traction. The recording of data over a longer period of time (about 100 hours) with slow paper tape speeds allows for the recognition of similarities in 24-hour cycles of interference levels. This is the result of the work schedule in a given mine (3-shift system, maximum coal output during the first shift) and is related to the frequency of trains running in headings, in which the telephone lines are located. Therefore, we restricted our measurements to a single (the first) shift, as being the most representative, to obtain the value of the interference voltages.

TABLE 5.11   Values of harmonics U_f of the interference voltage U in the telephone

Mine denotation	KWK 1				KWK 3	
circuit no.	6141		6418	6468	26	42
f [Hz]	mV					
50	0.56	—[1]	0.85	0.03–0.05	2.1	—
82	11	7	12.3	0.71	—[2]	—[2]
164	1.5	1.1	1.6	0.08	—[2]	—[2]
300	3.1	0.005	0.2	0.15–0.24	3.7	0.28
600	2.0	0.005	0.07	0.09–0.1	1.8–3	0.13
900	1.4	0.005	0.11	0.075–0.09	0.85	0.15
1200	0.71			0.04–0.09	2.8–3.5	0.35
1500					0.42	0.13–0.15
U [dB]	−31	−43	−36--−47	−58--−63	−38--−66	−61--−62
U_p [dB]	−66	−73	−68--−70	−73	−50--−70	−75

Notes: (1) Measurements on Sunday — traction off
      (2) the mine has no dispatching loudspeaking system of ALGUS type
      (3) in the case of switching on a TRG-1 radiotelephone, the level of voltage with the frequency of 100 kHz was contained within the range from −38 dB to −13 dB

Examples of simultaneous records of the unweighted level of interference and of the 300 Hz harmonic in a telephone circuit of one of the coal mines is presented in Fig. 5.23. The records were made on Sunday, before connecting the APSPa rectifier stations and during the working week. During one exploitation shift (about 17^{30}, as can be seen in the diagram) an instantaneous, emergency break in the voltage supplying the electric trolley traction system took place. Records presented in Fig. 5.24 were obtained at a higher recording speed, whereas in Fig. 5.25 examples of the measurements of the unweighted voltage level and the 300 Hz voltage are given, both as recorded using detectors with high and low (1 s) time constants. Numerical results are given in Table 5.10. The results of the analysis of harmonic are presented in Table 5.11. They also include the interference produced by the ALGUS system, by the ATI-CB set calling signal and by radiotelephones; the level of the unweighted interference voltage U and the level of the psophometric voltage U_p are also given.

circuits of underground coal mines being analysed

KWK 8	KWK 9		KWK 10		
177	6262	6438	6304	6305	6307
mV					
0.6	0.03	0.01	0.09	0.18	0.5
—[2]	0.26	0.33	—[2]	—[2]	—[2]
—[2]	0.02	0.01	—[2]	—[2]	—[2]
1.1–2.8	0.03–0.31	0.01–0.5	1.1–6.5	0.2–6.5	0.07–0.13
0.13–0.66	0.02–0.22	0.6	0.4–1.9	0.7–1.8	0.14
0.18	0.01–0.09	0.5	0.2–0.7	0.4–1.1	0.06
0.22	0.01–0.22	0.16	0.9	0.4–0.9	0.02
0.04–0.09					
−48−−62	−60−−65	−57	−51	−45−−48[3]	−61
−66−−67	−62−−75	−59	−68	−52	−75

5.9   Interference produced by the operation of radiotelephones

Radiotelephones of the TRG-1 type are used in the transport vehicles of electric trolley traction systems. A circuit (asymmetrical in practice) made of the trolley wire and the rails is used to propagate signals. An account of the structure of the traction network (the division into sections and zones of supply and the supply of illumination from a contact wire), the network has to be adapted to the requirements of communication in order to secure communication throughout an entire level.

Such an adaptation consists of the installation of stop filters at all the power (OZ-400B) and illumination (DZ-06, DZ-1, DZ-2) inlets and outlets, which substantially decreases the attenuation of these receivers. It is also necessary to make by-passes which make it possible for a usable signal to pass between the various supply zones (from different APSPa rectifier stations) of a contact wire. These by-passes are made by leading the usable trolleyphone signal (100 kHz) through the circuits of telephone cables, or through separate single-core cables laid beside telephone cables, and by connecting the individual sections of the traction network with this cable or with a telephone cable (using an

SP-750 connecting box). A schematic diagram of these principles is shown in Fig. 5.26 [49].

A high level signal may be introduced, asymmetrically with respect to the earth, into a telephone cable, which could cause significant cross-talk into other circuits contained in this cable. This may be the cause of cross-talk between the trolleyphone communication systems on different mine levels, which may result in the possibility of serious accident. Moreover, when a by-pass is contained in a cable, it is impossible to accept other circuits contained in this cable as being intrinsically safe. In such cases, in methane-rich mines, the by-passes should be made in a separate cable, or in telephone cables which do not contain intrinsically safe circuits.

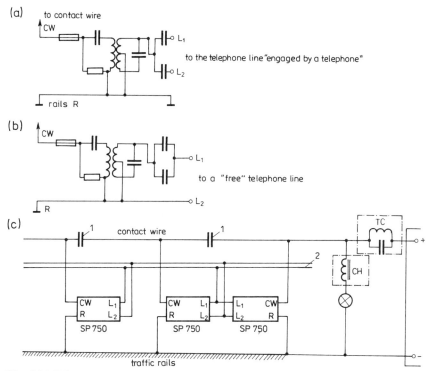

Fig. 5.26 Schematic diagram of a connection box of the SP-750 type and examples of its use for connecting telecommunication circuits used in radiotelephone communication (a), (b), and the method of adapting a traction network (c); CH, TC—chokes (DZ type) and a band-stop filter (OZ type): 1—section insulator, 2—by-pass circuit in a telephone cable

To examine the influence of the operation of radiotelephones, measurements of the variation on the interference voltage over 24-hours in teletransmission cables were carried out, with separation of the interference with the frequency of radiotelephone operation; a comparison of the two measurements allows an assessment of the cross-talk voltage induced by trolleyphones into teletransmission circuits. Example of the records of the level of the voltage U, measured at the terminals of an intrinsically safe subscriber line in a telephone exchange of one of the mines is presented in Fig. 5.27. This line was loaded with a telephone set at the underground side, while the voltage in the exchange was measured with a meter with a 600 Ω input impedance and an attached recording device. The results of the measurements reveal that interference voltages in telecommunication circuits, generated by trolleyphones are sinusoidal in nature, with a duration not exceeding twenty seconds as a rule with intervals lasting for as much as a few minutes. Longer intervals between interferences (of order of two hours) from radiotelephones can only be observed between shifts (e.g. between 13^{00} and 15^{00} or 5^{00} and 7^{00}).

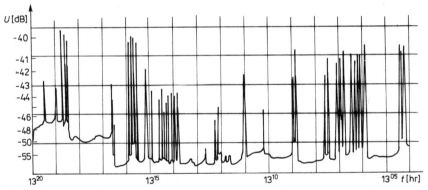

Fig. 5.27 Record of the interference voltage (unweighted) in a mine telephone line (KWK 10); 0 dB $\hat{=}$ 0.775 V

During days off no interference voltages from trolleyphones were observed. The interference voltages coming from trolleyphones depend on the scheduling of wheel transport on a given mine level, the frequency of train movement, network failure and the state of train safety systems, etc. Partial results of the measurements are presented in Table 5.12. They

TABLE 5.12   Influence of the operation of TRG-1 radiotelephones upon the levels of interference in mine branch subscribers lines (example for 4 mines)

KWK	No. of branch lines	Unweighted wide-band voltages, in a circuit — radiotelephone inoperative [dB]	Selective voltage ($f = 100$ kHz) in a circuit during operating of a radiotelephone [dB]	Notes
5	16	−80	−31−−38	by-passes incorporated in common telecommunication cables
8	177 (at 300 mining level)	−62	−58 −41 −70	200| levels of mine, at which radio- 300| telephone was operated 600|
	187 (at 200 level)	−58	−44 −48 −54	200| levels of mine, at which radio- 300| telephone was operated 600|
9	6133 6132 6432	−64−−70 −60 −58	−54−−70 −50 −38	by-passes in separate telephone cables
10	6304 6305	−51 −45	−38 −13	by-passes in common telecommunication cables

reveal that the values of cross-talk from the trolleyphones into cable lines range from -60 dB to -20 dB. In rare cases values of up to -13 dB are reached. This high variability in cross-talk voltages is the result of the fact that the measurements were sometimes made in telephone circuits, which transversed levels with neither cable traction systems nor TRG-1 radiotelephones. Leading the by-passes out of the telecommunication cables reduces the cross-talk voltage by about 20 dB. The cross-talk voltages originating from radiotelephones have frequencies of 100 kHz or 120 kHz and form a primary consideration in designing underground TDM (time division multiplexing) digital telephone systems.

5.10   The influence of electric traction systems on the level of the interference voltage in radiotelephone loop antennas

In a wireless traction system (battery-driven or pneumatic) a symmetrical circuit consisting of two insulated wires suspended along both side walls of the headings is used for propagating the usable signal of radiotelephones. This symmetrical circuit (called a *loop antenna*) is inductively coupled with the frame antenna of a moving radiotelephone, located on the roof of a locomotive. Stationary radiotelephones are directly connected to the loop antenna. In mines, in which only some areas are considered to be dangerous with respect to explosions, both trolley and battery-driven traction systems are used. Both storage-battery and wire-fed (trolley) electric locomotives move along the same tracks. Communication with the drivers of both types of locomotives is ensured by the use of TRGI radiotelephones and a loop antenna. Operational experience reveals that the quality of communication is unsatisfactory, when the loop antenna is located in headings with wire-fed locomotives, or when storage-battery locomotives equipped with thyristor systems (choppers) are used. The large dimensions of a radiotelephone (TRGI-1R) and the lack of space in a locomotive, the unreliability of the power supply, together with the frequent damage to loop antennas, have caused these radiotelephones to be used reluctantly in mines [51]. Difficult mining and geological conditions (narrowing of cross-headings), the numerous air-locks on the locomotive tracks, and cables and pipelines under the roofs on one hand, and the large size of the frame antenna ($828 \times 428 \times 125$ mm) on a locomotive on the other, cause the frame antennas to be frequently damaged. Therefore, apart from attempts at using smaller antennas and flexible frame antennas for the TRGI-1R radiotelephones, ferrite antennas, with parameters considerably better than those of the frame antennas used so far, are now being introduced.

The measurements carried out on loop antennas used for TRGI-1P radiotelephone communication were aimed at determining the variability with time, spectral characteristics and maximum values of the interference voltages. These measurements were conducted using a NLMZ-4 interference meter (with peak detector) and a system for recording meter readings within the frequency range of 10 kHz to 150 kHz, in a heading with a double-track electric contact traction system. A variable length loop antenna (200, 750 and 2400 m) was made from a LY (1×4 mm^2) cable, and was suspended under the insulators of the transverse ropes supporting the contact wire. Suspending the loop in this manner considerably reduced the accidental earthing of this antenna and ensured its high symmetry relative to earth. The measurements were carried out in the following situations: (a) no voltage applied to the contact wire, (b) contact wire connected to an APSPa station and loaded with illumination devices, (c) electric locomotive driven according to the traffic cycle presented in Fig. 4.5a (for each measurement the frequency was determined with an NLMZ-4 meter).

Figure 5.28 presents the variation of the interference voltage with the frequency $f = 100$ kHz for half of the electric locomotive traffic cycle,

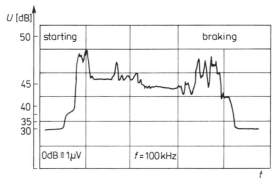

Fig. 5.28 Record of the interference voltage (in a loop antenna) with a frequency of 100 kHz during the operation of an electric locomotive of the type Ld31

whereas Fig. 5.29 presents the frequency characteristics of the interference voltage measured in a loop antenna 750 m long for different states of traction operation [51]. The analysis of the results of voltages measurements in antennas of different length reveals that:

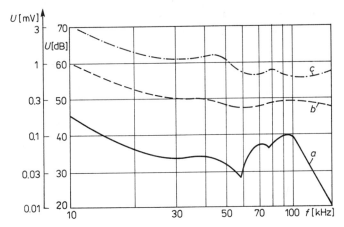

Fig. 5.29 Values of the interference voltage in a loop antenna (750 m) caused by electric cable traction: a—disconnected contact wire, b—connected contact wire—supply for illumination lamps, c—normal operation of locomotives

— in the case of a complete lack of voltage in a contact wire, the interference voltages in loop antennas range from 10 µV to 100 µV (for 100 kHz) and are clearly lower than the threshold of radiotelephone noise suppression,

— connecting the APSPa station causes an increase in the interference voltage in loop antennas, however, its maximum level (for 100 kHz) is below the radiotelephone noise suppression threshold,

— the level of interference voltage measured with the electric locomotive moving ranges from 10 µV to 10 mV and very clearly depends on the technological condition and type of operation of an electric locomotive (starting, breaking, change of speed), sparking at the pantograph and locomotive wheels and on the condition of the traction network,

— earthing the loop antenna causes an increase in the interference voltage from 10 to 15 dB.

Storage-battery locomotives only exert an influence when they are

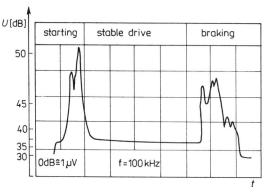

Fig. 5.30 Interference voltage with 100 Hz frequency in a loop antenna, during the drive of a thyristor-equipped storage-battery locomotive

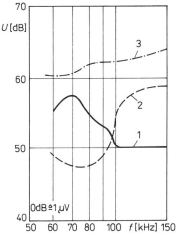

Fig. 5.31 Values of interference voltage in function of the frequency, induced by the operation of a storage-battery locomotive of the Lea BM12/3T type in loop antennas with the lengths of: 1—200 m, 2—750 m, 3—2450 m

equipped with a thyristor regulator (locomotives of the Lea BM 12/3T type); an example of this is given in Figs. 5.30 and 5.31. A voltage of the order of 20–50 dB relative to 1 μV (for $f = 100$ kHz) is induced in a frame antenna on the roof of a locomotive. The threshold of the TRGI-1R radiotelephone noise suppression is from 300 μV up to 3 mV, which corresponds to 49.5–69.5 dB relative to 1 μV. At the level of a usable signal corresponding to the maximum sensitivity of a radiotelephone, the noise margin is not enough and the operation of the chopper is clearly heard in the TRGI-1 radiotelephone speaker.

5.11 The influence of interference on the operation of radiotelephone receivers

A radiotelephone receiver is a system with a band-pass frequency characteristic called a receiver selectivity curve. Figure 5.32 presents the selectivity curve of a TRG-1k radiotelephone receiver as the relationship between the ratio of the voltage at the limiter input U_l to the maximum voltage at the limiter input $U_{l\max}$ and the frequency at a constant level of receiver input voltage. The receiver selectivity curve defines the so-called

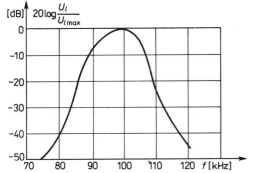

Fig. 5.32 Selectivity of a mine radiotelephone receiver of the type TRG-1k

basic channel of the receiver. In receivers with direct amplification, the basic channel is, in fact, the only one, through which the signals from the receiver input pass to its output. In receivers with frequency conversion, parasite channels can appear, through which interference can penetrate the receiver. To explain the mechanism of parasite channel formation, it is necessary to discuss a portion of the block diagram of a receiver with frequency conversion presented in Fig. 5.33.

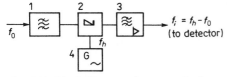

Fig. 5.33 Block diagram of a system for frequency conversion: 1—input filter, 2—mixer, 3—intermediate frequency amplifier, 4—oscillator of frequency converter circuit (heterodyne)

The basic channel of a receiver is defined by the frequency

$$f_0 = f_h - f_i. \tag{5.17}$$

In a receiver, there may occur the following parasite channels, corresponding to an image frequency:

$$f_m = f_h + f_i, \tag{5.18}$$

to an intermediate frequency f_i and to the frequencies defined by the harmonics of a heterodyne (oscillator of frequency converter),

$$f_{0h} = f_{hn} - f_i, \tag{5.19}$$

where

f_{hn} — n-th harmonic of the heterodyne.

Another path of interference signal permeation is through the phenomena caused by the non-linearity of the elements in receiver input circuits, such as intermodulation and cross-modulation [29]. Intermodulation refers to the condition where the non-linearity of the characteristics of elements operating in the receiver input circuit causes a frequency conversion. The sum of non-sinusoidal signals permeating into a non-linear element (e.g. a transistor) is given by

$$u_{\text{in}} = U_1 \cos \omega' t + U_2 \cos \omega'' t \tag{5.20}$$

while the non-linear characteristics of the transistor can be presented in the form

$$i_{\text{out}} = g_m u_{\text{in}} + \tfrac{1}{2} g'_m u_{\text{in}}^2 + \tfrac{1}{6} g''_m u_{\text{in}}^3, \tag{5.21}$$

where

g_m — gradient of transistor characteristics,

g'_m, g''_m — derivatives of characteristics curve.

After substituting (5.20) to (5.21) and applying appropriate trigonometric transformations we obtain components with the following pulsations: $\omega' + \omega''$, $\omega' - \omega''$, $2\omega'$, $2\omega''$, $3\omega'$, $3\omega''$, $2\omega' - \omega''$, $2\omega' + \omega''$, $2\omega'' - \omega'$, $2\omega'' + \omega'$. The components listed here may permeate into a receiver through parasite channels and through the basic channel.

Cross-modulation arises due to the fact that a modulated interference signal with a frequency beyond the basic band of a receiver causes an additional modulation of the usable signal due to the existence of non-linearity. Let the sum of the usable and interference signals in the form of

$$u_{in} = U_s(1 + m_s \cos\omega_s t)\cos\Omega_s t + U_{int}(1 + m_{int}\cos\omega_{int} t)\cos\Omega_{int} t, \quad (5.22)$$

permeate onto the input of a non-linear element, where

U_s — maximum (amplitue) value of a usable signal,
m_s — modulation depth of usable signal,
Ω_s — usable signal carrier pulsation,
ω_s — pulsation modulating the usable signal,
U_{int} — maximum value of interference signal,
m_{int} — modulation depth of interference signal,
ω_{int} — pulsation modulating the interference signal,
Ω_{int} — interference signal carrier pulsation.

After substituting (5.22) to (5.21), applying suitable simplifications and neglecting harmonics and combined frequencies we obtain

$$i_{out} \approx g_m U_s(1 + m_s \cos\omega_s t + \frac{1}{2} m_{int} U_{int} \frac{g''_m}{g'_m} \cos\omega_{int} t)\cos\Omega_s t. \quad (5.23)$$

Equation (5.23) shows that non-linearity causes amplitude cross modulation of a usable signal. The depth of cross-modulation is equal to

$$m_{cr} = \frac{1}{2} m_{int} U_{int}^2 \frac{g''_m}{g'_m}. \quad (5.24)$$

The mechanism of cross-modulation presented above may be the reason for permeation of interference in AM receivers.

It can be proved that the non-linearity of amplifier components does not cause the FM cross-modulation. In FM receivers, cross-modulation is caused by the fact that an amplitude-modulated interfering signal may cause both amplitude and frequency modulation of a heterodyne output voltage.

Under mining conditions, the sum of an appropriately modulated usable signal (FM in case of Polish long-wave receivers) and an interference signal with a spectrum covering the basic channel is fed onto the input of receivers. The presence of interference with a frequency spectrum covering the basic channel at the receiver input is the cause of signal distortion at a receiver output (a loudspeaker).

An analysis of the influence of interference upon the operation of a receiver has been worked out for the case when the sum of the usable

signal and a white noise is fed into the receiver input. For the purpose of
the analysis, block diagrams of receivers as presented in Fig. 5.34 were
used [14].

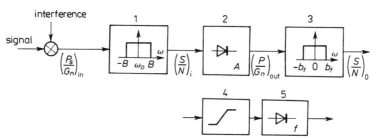

Fig. 5.34 Block diagram of a radiotelephone receiver: 1—pre-detection filter with
        rectangular characteristics and with a width of $2B$, 2—amplitude detector (for
        AM), 3—sub-detection low-pass filter with width b_f, 4—amplitude limiter (for
        FM), 5—frequency detector (for FM)

The influence of interference upon the quality of reception is
determined by the ratio of the mean usable signal power P_{outs} to the mean
noise power P_{outn} at the receiver output

$$\frac{P_{outs}}{P_{outn}} = \left(\frac{S}{N}\right)_0. \tag{5.25}$$

The $(S/N)_0$ value depends on the ratio of the mean usable signal power
at the receiver input P_{ins} to the mean noise power at the output of
a pre-detection filter P_{inn}

$$\left(\frac{S}{N}\right)_i = \frac{P_{ins}}{P_{inn}}. \tag{5.26}$$

The P_{inn} power is determined from the equation

$$P_{inn} = \int_{-\infty}^{\infty} G_{inn}(\omega)\,|H_{in}(j\omega)|^2\,d\omega, \tag{5.27}$$

where
    $G_{inn}(\omega)$—spectral density of noise power at a receiver input,
    $H_{in}(j\omega)$—frequency transfer function of a pre-detection filter.
The relationship

$$\left(\frac{S}{N}\right)_0 = f\left(\frac{S}{N}\right)_i \tag{5.28}$$

is called the *modulation noise characteristic*, whereas the ratio

$$g = \frac{\left(\dfrac{S}{N}\right)_0}{\left(\dfrac{S}{N}\right)_i} \tag{5.29}$$

is called the *modulation gain*.

In the case of a white noise at the receiver input $(G_{inn}(\omega) = G_{inn} = \text{const})$ the relation

$$g' = \frac{\dfrac{P_{outs}}{G_{outn}}}{\dfrac{P_{ins}}{G_{inn}}} = \frac{\left(\dfrac{S}{N}\right)_0}{\left(\dfrac{S}{N}\right)_i}\frac{b_f}{2B} = \frac{b_f}{2B}g \tag{5.30}$$

is called the *relative (reference) modulation gain*. The values of g and g' depend on the type and parameters of modulation, detector structure and $(S/N)_i$. For high $(S/N)_i$ values, modulation gains do not depend on $(S/N)_i$, and assume the following values:

AM and linear envelope detection

$$g_{AM} = 2\frac{m^2 x^2}{1 + m^2 x^2}, \tag{5.31}$$

AM and square envelope detection

$$g_{AM} = 2\frac{1}{1 + 2m^2 x^2}\frac{m^2 x^2}{1 + m^2 x^2}, \tag{5.32}$$

$$g'_{AM} = 2\frac{1}{1 + 2m^2 x^2}\frac{m^2}{1 + m^2 x^2}, \tag{5.33}$$

FM

$$g_{FM} = 3x^2 m_f^2 \frac{2B}{b_f}, \tag{5.34}$$

$$g'_{FM} = 3x^2 m_f^2, \tag{5.35}$$

where

$\varkappa$ — ratio of value of modulation signal to maximum value of modulating signal,

m — modulation depth,

m_f — modulation index.

In the case of low $(S/N)_i$ values, threshold phenomena occur, which cause a loss of modulation gain and a non-linearity of characteristics $(S/N)_0 = f(S/N)_i$.

For the amplitude modulation using the full spectrum of a modulated signal (main spectral and two sidebands) the modulation gain is smaller than unity (equations (5.31)–(5.33)). In the case of the most frequently used envelope detectors, which have low $(S/N)_i$ values, there occurs a threshold effect consisting in a reduction of the g_{AM} value. Figure 5.35

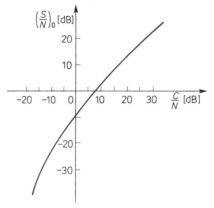

Fig. 5.35 Noise characteristics of a square amplitude detection ($\varkappa^2 = 0.5$, $m = 1$, C/N — ratio of the power of the carrier signal to the noise power at the receiver input) [14]

presents an example of AM noise characteristics for a square detector with $\varkappa^2 = \frac{1}{2}$ (sinusoidal modulating signal) and $m = 1$. For $(C/N)_i < 10$ dB, non-linearity of characteristics occurs, which leads to a reduction of the value of g. Frequency modulation at modulation indices which are not excessively low ($m_f > 1$) and at high $(g/N)_i$ values always has a modulation gain of greater than 1. If the $(S/N)_i$ value is reduced, a threshold effect occurs, which leads to a substantial reduction of g_{FM} (even below 1) and non-linearity of noise characteristics. The $(S/N)_i$ value, at which such non-linearity first occurs, is called the *noise threshold*. Figure 5.36 presents the modulation noise characteristics for a conventional frequency detector. For $(S/N)_i < 20$ dB, characteristic inflexions (noise thresholds) can be seen.

The noise threshold can be lowered by using an appropriately designed FM detector, such as for example detectors with feed back, detectors with a synchronized phase or detectors with a synchronized frequency. More detailed information concerning the subject of threshold properties of FM detectors can be found in reference [14].

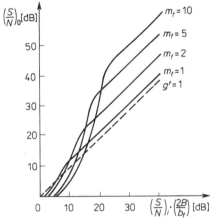

Fig. 5.36 Noise characteristics of frequency detection ($x^2 = 0.5$); broken line denotes the characteristic for single-sideband amplitude modulation with suppressed carrier frequency (AM-SSB-SC)

An increase of the $(S/N)_0$ values for FM is obtained by using a pre-emphasis and de-emphasis which involves the shaping of appropriate frequency characteristics for low-frequency amplifiers in both receiver and transmitter. For radiotelephones it is assumed that the pre-emphasis characteristics (of a low-frequency transmitter amplifier) increases by 6 dB per octave within the frequency range from 300 to 3000 Hz, and the de-emphasis characteristics (of a low-frequency receiver amplifier) decreases by 6 dB per octave, within the frequencies range from 300 to 3000 Hz. The results of the measurements of long-wave radiotelephone de-emphasis characteristics for mining radiotelephones (TRGI) stand in good agreement with the requirements presented.

Besides noise interference, receiver operation is also influenced by pulse interference. Receiver immunity to pulse interference is determined for a system as presented in Fig. 5.37, using a psophometer with radio filter (Fig. 5.38).

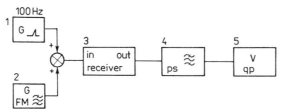

Fig. 5.37 Principle of measurement of radiotelephone receiver immunity to pulse interference: 1—generator of pulses with a frequency of repetition of 100 Hz, 2—generator of measuring signal (signal with operating frequency, modulated with a sinusoid signal of 1000 Hz with a permissible frequency deviation of 30%), 3—receiver, 4—psophometric radio filter (characteristics as in Fig. 5.38), 5—quasi-peak voltmeter with envelope detector with a charging time constant of $t_e = 2$ ms and that of discharging $t_d = 60$ ms

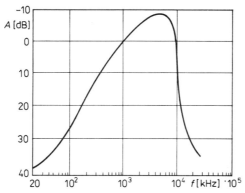

Fig. 5.38 Frequency characteristics of the attenuation A of a psophometric radio filter

Receiver immunity to pulse interference O_i is given by the equation [29]

$$O_i = 20 \log \frac{U_s}{U_{int}}, \tag{5.36}$$

where

U_s — value of the usable signal voltage at the receiver output with interferene pulse generator off,

U_{int} — quasi-peak value of the interference voltage at the receiver output with measuring signal generator modulation off.

An example of the relationship between the receiver immunity to pulse interference and the level of usable signal s at the receiver input with various surface S of interference pulses is presented in Fig. 5.39. The method presented above can be used for the evaluation of the resistance of radio receivers to pulse interference. It seems, that by using a telephone psophometric filter it could also be used for evaluating the resistance of the radiotelephone receiver to pulse interference.

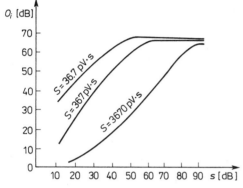

Fig. 5.39 Example of the characteristics of an immunity O_i of radiotelephone receiver to pulse interference

5.12 Methane monitoring systems

In Polish coal mining, the CTT63/40U system (Fig. 5.40) and its modifications using the modular CMM-20 and digital CMC-1 methane detection centres are mostly used for the periodical measurement of methane concentration in mine air [19, 20]. The modifications of methane detection centres (master stations) used up-to-date consist mainly of the use of NSK/V/61g recorders (in the CMM-20 centre) and the use of a minicomputer (PRS-4). These modifications did not change the mode of operation of the methane detection systems. At present, a multifunctional masterstation with a microprocessor of the CWμP-1 type is being built. The principal element of this system consists of a methane detection centre, to which, through a block of protective barriers PBB, up to 40 circuits (in four groups—A, B, C, D—of ten circuits each) are connected, which connect the master station with either low methane concentration detectors (of the type CMI), or with high methane concentration detectors (of the type CKA).

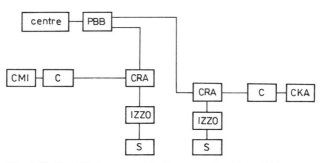

Fig. 5.40 Simplified structural diagram of a CTT63/40U system: PBB—protective barrier block, CRA—switching-off device, C—coder, CMI, CKA—sensors, IZZO—intrinsically safe interface, S—power network switch

Methane concentration measurements carried out by individual detectors are performed in cycles, for periods of 5 s. The measurement cycle is as follows:

circuits A1 to A10 — 10×5 s = 50 s
interval   10 s
circuits B1 to B10 — 10×5 s = 50 s
interval   10 s
circuits C1 to C10 — 10×5 s = 50 s
interval   10 s
circuits D1 to D10 — 10×5 s = 50 s
interval   10 s

Total: 40 circuits and 4 intervals: 240 s (4 min).

The low-methane concentration detector (CNI) operates on the principle of catalytic CH_4 combustion. There are two coils in the test chamber: a detection coil FD and compensation coil FC, which form the branches of a test bridge (Fig. 5.41). The detector is supplied from a battery, located in the coder, with a current of 870 mA. When methane is burnt on the detection coil in the test chamber, it causes an increase in its temperature (resistance) and thus, an imbalance of the test bridge. In the coder a converter changes the imbalanced bridge voltage into frequency. The relationship between the converter frequency and the methane concentration is as follows:

0% CH_4—10 kHz,
2% CH_4—8 kHz.

In the intervals between the measurements, the battery in the coder is disconnected for the coder and the electronic detector system, and is being loaded from the detection centre by the 27 mA current. The taking of the measurements is caused by a change in the polarization of the current in the circuit supplying the coder. The coder "questioning" current is equal to 13 mA and its polarity is reverse to that of the battery charging current.

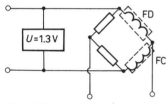

Fig. 5.41 Schematic diagram of a low methane concentration detector (CMI)

During the measurement, the voltage signal from the output of the coder converter is sent, after amplification, to the methane detection centre. In the methane detection centre, the methane concentration which has been measured is being compared with the threshold value of the given detector. If the methane concentration exceeds the threshold value, the detection centre sends an alarm signal. This signal changes the direct charging current into a rectangular signal at intervals lasting for 5 ms every 250 ms. Such a signal does not interfere with the measurements and only influences the switching-off devices (CRA—Fig. 5.42). During battery charging, in the coder (interval between measurements), circuit polarization (like in Fig. 5.42) causes excitation of the relay P.

Polarization inversion during measurements (5 s) does not de-excite the relay P due to time constant of condenser C_7 discharge equal to 15 s. The alarm signal causes the condenser C_4 to be charged through the diode pumps C_3, D_5, D_6. When the voltage on the C_4 condenser reaches the required value, the following happens: the T_1 transistor is saturated,

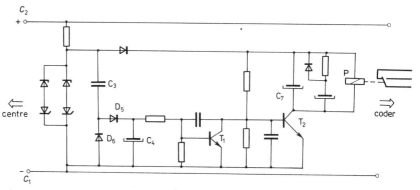

Fig. 5.42 Simplified schematic diagram of a CRA switching-off device

the T_2 transistor is locked, and the relay P is de-excited. De-excitation of
the relay P causes a switching-off of the electricity supply, for example
through a switch in the ROK 6 switchgear. The intrinsically safe output
of the CRA device cannot be connected to usually non-intrinsically safe
switch control circuits. In such a case, it is necessary to use an
intermediate device (IZZO). The intrinsic safety of the underground part
is achieved by using protective barriers (Fig. 5.43). However, earthing
one of barrier terminals causes asymmetrical loading of transmission
circuits.

After using the CTT 63/40U system in the mines with contact electric
traction or high power converter drives (e.g. hoisting machines),
improper operation of the CTT 63/40U system has been discovered. In
particular, the asymmetry of circuit loading causes an increase of the
interference voltage level at the masterstation input, which, when
combined with a wide-band voltage to frequency converter in the
masterstation, causes unjustified shut-downs of electric energy. This
situation was improved when an LC filter of the FP6-15/40 type, with

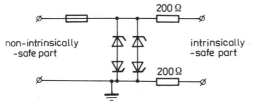

Fig. 5.43 Schematic diagram of a protection barrier

a pass band of 4.5–12 kHz was used. An example of the spectrum of the interference voltage U_f, measured in methane detection circuits in a mine with an electric contact traction system is presented in Fig. 5.44. This voltage spectrum is characterized by a high level of interference originating in the traction system (multiples of 300 Hz). The use of the FP6 filter substantially reduces the r.m.s. value of the interference at the

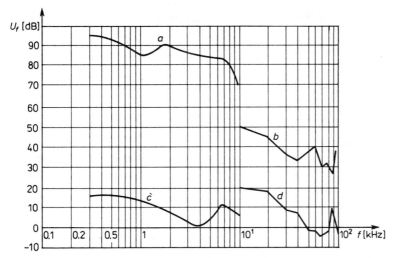

Fig. 5.44 Interference spectrum in a methane detection circuit: *a, c*—envelope of the spectrum of interference voltages, measured with a heterodyne analyser for an asymmetric (*a*) and symmetric (*c*) load on the circuit; *b, d*—peak values of interference voltages measured with interference meter in a circuit loaded asymmetrically (*b*) and symmetrically (*d*)

master station input [30]. In a digital methane master station (CMC-1), the measurement of the methane concentration is preceded by the measurement of interference voltages, which allows a reduction in the number of unnecessary power shut-downs caused by high instantaneous levels of interference. Further improvements in the resistance of methane detection systems to electromagnetic interference may be achieved by designing transmission systems, which ensure symmetrical circuit loading.

5.13   Some requirements and general principles of the protection of telecommunication lines against electromagnetic interference

A desirable state of electromagnetic compatibility of telecommunication networks can be obtained using passive and active coordination methods. Therefore, it is necessary to take into account both the requirements concerned with the principles of structure and operation of a power network and of the devices of an electric traction network which constitute the principal sources of electromagnetic interference, and the requirements relating to the design, manufacture and operation of telecommunication networks.

5.13.1   Basic requirements for reducing the interference produced in power lines

The reduction of electromagnetic sinusoidal interference, the source of which most often lies in power networks and devices, can be achieved by using networks operating with an unearthed system, with an insulated zero point. In such a network, prophylactic means are possible (and they should be used), which first of all monitor the condition of earth return insulation, reduce the duration time of possible earthings, and also reduce the probability of the occurrence of line-to-line short-circuits.

If there is a justified need to use elements with non-linear characteristics in a mine network (e.g. semi-conductor converters), it should be designed so as to limit as far as possible the generation of harmonic voltages and currents, and the possibility of their propagation through electric lines. It also may be indispensable to use appropriately selected filters (maintained in good operative condition) limiting the harmonics of interference. Instances where thyristor converters are used in mine networks should be analysed in detail and thoroughly checked with regard to the possibility and range of electromagnetic interference generated by them and possible effects.

Assuming that the currents leaking from electric networks may appear as stray voltages (currents) in different parts of the electric circuits of a mine, including telecommunication circuits, it is advisable to attempt to undertake actions leading to:

— reduction of the use of earth as a part of an electric circuit,

— ensuring the symmetry of a three-phase system phases load and of parameters relative to earth,

— obtaining appropriate internal impedance for the sources (transformers), which reduces the values of short-circuit currents and, at
the same time, makes it possible to quickly shut-down the
short-circuits.

Reduction of the interference produced by harmonics of the network
and pulse interference is, among others, obtained through:

— a reduction of the voltage supplying those elements with
non-linear magnetization characteristics (iron cores),
— the use of rectifiers with the greatest possible number of phases,
— the use of appropriate anti-interference devices (screens,
smoothing filters, coil and trap circuits, anti-interference condensers) especially in the case of thyristor converters, commutator
motors and other spark-producing elements,
— ensuring a high conductivity of the bottom network of a contact
electric traction system and a good insulation between the rails
and the ground.

The rectifier stations supplying the underground traction networks
(250 V) should be equipped with smoothing devices, which ensure the
reduction of the interference voltage at the station outlet to the
equivalent of 5–10% of the rated voltage. These devices should be
carefully looked after and maintained in prime operating condition
(regular checking and turning of the resonance circuits, immediate repair
of possible defects). Rectifier assemblies of neighbouring stations
(supplying the same traction network) should be identical with regard to
the number of phases and the method of connecting.

Constructing the traction return circuit (rails), so as to ensure the
protection of metallic underground devices against corrosion, is of the
utmost importance; also from the point of view of the reduction of the
interaction of the traction line with neighbouring telecommunication
lines through magnetic and galvanic couplings.

5.13.2 *The symmetry of transmission lines*

A reduction of the influence of heavy current interference upon
telecommunication circuits can be obtained by using symmetrical
teletransmission circuits. Circuit symmetry should be considered first of
all relative to the earth and load, and relative to the source of
interference, whereas the devices connected to the circuit should also not
significantly disturb this symmetry.

An appropriate symmetry of a circuit relative to the earth results in the interference voltages between the wire of the line and the earth (in case of electric coupling) or the electromotive force induced in each of the two wires of a side circuit (in case of magnetic coupling) being at least approximately equal. A condition of symmetry with respect to the source of interference and receiver load makes it possible to avoid current flow in the receiver connected to the circuit. Obtaining an appropriate symmetry relative to earth is practically always possible in cable circuits, provided they are properly built and maintained. It is especially important that the following two basic requirements should be met.

Transmission circuits should be made up of one pair of cores with a common twist or within a quad with a common twist (Fig. 5.3). Pairing neighbouring cores of quads results in an asymmetry of the circuit capacity relative to earth. Therefore, none of the circuit cores should be connected with the earth; earthing results in an asymmetry of the capacity (impedance, see Fig. 5.12) of side circuits and neighbouring circuits.

The insulation of the circuits should be well protected against moisture. Moisture on cables or on their connections and endings may exert a substantial influence upon the symmetry of the impedance relative to earth. Therefore, in underground mine workings, teletransmission cables in water-tight sheaths (metallic or equivalent ones would be the best) should be used. Cable connections and endings should be made in cable boxes, cable heads and appropriate connecting boxes and cubicles, appropriately sealed with cable filling compound, synthetic resin or in some other, equivalent manner.

Even when the other conditions are met, the symmetry of teletransmission circuits also depends on the nature of the telecommunication devices connected with the circuit. All the devices included in the circuit or connected to it should change the properties of both conductors (pair) to the same extent. Any asymmetric device can be included in a symmetric circuit only in conjunction with balancing devices (transformers).

5.13.3   Requirements concerning the design of telecommunication lines

Transmission circuits and telecommunication devices connected with them, which may be subjected to the electromagnetic interaction of power lines, should be designed and made in the form of symmetric circuits. Symmetry relative to earth is particularly important (this does not apply to co-axial circuits). Asymmetry attenuation should be at least 40 dB (CCITT) for the frequency range of 300–3400 Hz. Any asymmetrical telecommunication devices should be connected to the symmetrical circuits through special linear transformers (if this is possible for the transmission method used).

Telecommunication lines and devices, which may be located within the zone of interaction of power lines, should be appropriately designed and constructed with particular care. This applies first of all to the appropriate choice of cables (e.g. with metallic, screened sheaths and with polyethylene insulation) and their associated devices. Cable joints, particularly in underground networks, should be made in such a way that they ensure a satisfactory protection against environmental conditions, and especially against water, dust, moisture, conductive contaminations and corrosive gases. In all the cable joints, the conducting sheaths, screens and armouring should be well (galvanically) connected with one another and with the neighbouring lengths of lines (cables); the condition of the joints should be checked regularly. Cable terminals which enter a telephone or dispatch exchange, should also be made in air-tight heads installed on earthered holders or stands. The earthing resistance should not exceed 5 Ω. Regular checking of the condition of the insulation and immediate repair of any damage is of great importance. In particular, periodical checks of the symmetry of impedance relative to earth of telecommunication circuits and devices should be carried out. Telcommunication lines should be separated from power lines. In order to comply with the regulations [80] and with the Polish standard PN-/E-05125, the following principles among others, of line construction (cabling) should be applied in mines:

— in headings, telecommunication and power cables should, if possible, be located on opposite side walls at a height of at least 1 m from the floor, and if this is not possible, the distance between them should be at least 0.3 m,
— telecommunication cables should be suspended from cable holders by flexible insulating pads,
— the crossing of telecommunication and power lines should be made at a right angle; the distance between both lines should be at least 30 cm (if not, the telecommunication cable should be protected with a steel tube, at least 60 cm long at a crossing).

To protect the telecommunication cables against the interaction of stray currents, means of reducing stray currents, anticorrosive screens, and insulated holders for cable suspension, should be used. When external insulation sheaths (e.g. anticorrosive screens for armouring) are used, earthing the cable sheaths and armouring connected with one another should be done only if the permissible value of the interference voltage caused by an electric traction line or other sources is exceeded. In such a case, in order to increase the reduction properties of a sheath and armouring, these should be connected to each other and earthed using condensers of appropriately selected capacities. Cables with thermoplastic anticorrosive screens should be installed in cable boxes in such a way that there is no metallic (galvanic) connection between the armouring or conducting (metallic) sheath and the body of the cable box.

As electric and acoustic shocks are possible, the speaking devices of manual exchanges and of telephone sets should be equipped with appropriate means for additional anti-shock protection. Telecommunication circuits, in which excess voltages caused by magnetic interaction of e.g. traction lines may occur, should be equipped with telecommunication overvoltage protectors installed in the main switchboard. Separating transformers (usually at the end of a circuit) can also be used if the transmission system used allows this. Earthing conductors of telecommunication devices should, if possible, be removed from the electrified railway lines or traction device earth electrodes.

References

[1] Bendayan, J., Emprin, P.: Perturbations, dans les cables de telecommunication, par les locomotives equipées de thiristor. *Cables et Transm.*, 1979, **2**.

[2] *CCITT*: Calculation of transverse voltage produced in telecommunication circuits by induction from electric railways or electric power line. Contribution November, 1979, **65**.

[3] *CCITT*: Calculation of electromagnetic induction of telecommunication cables by a numerical method for solvings a system of differential equations. Contribution December, 1979, **78**.

[4] Chernov, V. A., Chernova, N. N.: Mine telecommunication lines and their complex utilization. Moskva, Nedra, 1981 (in Russian).

[5] Dmitrev, T. A: Investigation of electric interference produced by asynchronous motors. Izv. VUZ, *Gornyi Zhurnal*, 1965, **1** (in Russian).

[6] Dvorak, Th. J.: Elektromagnetische Verträglichkeit—ein ernszunehmendes Problem der modernen Elektronik. *ETZ*, 1983, **17**.

[7] Electromagnetic compatibility measurements. Rhode Shwartz Co. materials, December, 1983.

[8] *Encyclopaedia of Modern Physics*, Warszawa, PWN, 1983 (in Polish).

[9] Frączek, S., Miśkiewicz, K., Wojaczek, A.: Investigations of the levels of voltages and currents in a 500 V district mine network within the frequency range above 300 Hz. *Proceedings of the XIIth Symposium of the Cybernetics in Mining Section*, Committee of Mining, Polish Academy of Sciences, "Theory and Technology of Information Transmission in Mining", Żelazno, 1983 (in Polish).

[10] Fuks, B. A., Szabat, B. W.: *The functions of a complex variable and some of their utilizations.* Warszawa, PWN, 1954 (in Polish).

[11] Goworkow, W. A.: *Electric and magnetic fields.* Warszawa, WNT, 1982 (in Polish).

[12] Il'in, A. A., Pelipenko, V. N.: *Dispatch communication in mining trolley networks.* Moskva, Izd. Nedra, 1964 (in Russian).

[13] Ivanchenko, E. A., Belan, N. A., Garin, Yu.M., Ogorodneichuk, I. F.: *Experimental investigation of low-frequency interference in low-voltage networks of mines.* Izv. VUZ, *Gornyi Zhurnal*, 1966, **11** (in Russian).

[14] Knoch, L., Ekiert, T.: *Modulation and detection.* Warszawa, WKŁ, 1979 (in Polish).

[15] Krakowski, M.: *Theoretical electrotechnics.* Warszawa, PWN, 1980 (in Polish).

[16] Krakowski, M.: *Earth-return circuits*. Warszawa, WNT, 1979 (in Polish).

[17] Krasucki, F.: Induced voltages in the auxiliary cores of power cables and mining trailing cables. *Archiwum Górnictwa*, 1970, **3** (in Polish).

[18] Krasucki, F.: *Electric hazards in mining*. Katowice, Wyd. "Śląsk", 1984 (in Polish).

[19] Krasucki, F., Musioł, K.: *Methane monitoring and methane detection security in mines*. Gliwice, Silesian Institute of Technology Press, 1981 (in Polish).

[20] Krasucki, F. (editor), Cierpisz, S.: Dispatch computer systems in underground coal mines. *Seminar on the electrification and automatization of mines*. Book 2. Gliwice, Silesian Institute of Technology Press, 1983 (in Polish).

[21] Laskowski, M., Markowski R.: Sources and levels of radioelectric interference in the Polish railway industry. *Przegląd Elektrotechniczny*, 1977, **3** (in Polish).

[22] Laskowski, M.: Localization of the main sources of radioelectric interference in electric traction vehicles. *Przegląd Elektrotechniczny*, 1977, **5** (in Polish).

[23] Łapiński, T.: Telecommunication mining cables with reduced screening coefficient. *Wiadomości Elektrotechniczne*, 1984, No. **9–10** (in Polish).

[24] Miśkiewicz, K.: Couplings between electric traction networks and telecommunication circuits in mining communication lines. *Proceedings of the XIIth Symposium of the Cybernetics in Mining Section*, Committee of Mining, Polish Academy of Sciences, "Theory and Technology of Information Transmission in Mining", Żelazno, 1983 (in Polish).

[25] Motohisa Kanda: Time and amplitude statistic for electromagnetic noise in mines. *IEEE Transaction on Electromagnetic Compatibility*, August, 1975, Vol. EMC-17, No. 3.

[26] Nowicki, W.: *Fundamentals of teletransmission*. Warszawa, WKŁ, 1974 (in Polish).

[27] Perkowski, Z., Łapiński, T.: *Modern telecommunication cables*. Warszawa, WKŁ, 1974 (in Polish).

[28] Piłotowicz, A.: *Interaction between electric power circuits and telecommunication circuits*. Warszawa, WKŁ, 1975 (in Polish).

[29] Rotkiewicz, W. (editor): *Electromagnetic compatibility in radio engineering*. Warszawa, WKŁ, 1978 (in Polish).

[30] *Reports of the Institute of Electrification and Automatization in Mining (IEAM)*, Silesian Institute of Technology (unpublished) (all in Polish):
 — Investigation of electromagnetic interference generated by underground electric traction networks, Gliwice, 1978,
 — Investigation of electromagnetic interference generated by electric power networks and the determination of the susceptibility to interference of telecommunication circuits, Gliwice, 1979,
 — Investigation of the susceptibility of telecommunication, signalling and control circuits to interference transmitted through electromagnetic couplings, Gliwice, 1980.

[31] *Reports of the IEAM*, Silesian Institute of Technology (unpublished) (all in Polish):
 — Investigation of interference of an electromagnetic nature in electric power networks and telecommunication networks in underground mines, Gliwice, 1981,
 — Problems of interference level standardization in telecommunication networks of mines, Gliwice, 1982,

— Statistical investigation of circuits and interference characteristics of underground telecommunication networks, Gliwice, 1983.

[32] *Reports of the Research and Production Centre (RPC) for Mining Electrotechnics and Automatics EMAG in Katowice:* Analysis and evaluation of telecommunication cables presently used in mining. Katowice, 1983 (unpublished) (in Polish).

[33] *Reports of RPC EMAG in Katowice:* The SET system of telephone communication-specifications. Katowice, 1981 (unpublished) (in Polish).

[34] Ratner, M. P.: *The inductive influence of electrified railway electric networks and pipelines.* Moskva, Izd. Transport, 1966 (in Russian).

[35] Rej, A., Skoropacki, W.: A mathematical model of mutual interaction between transmission circuits operating in a single telecommunication mining cable. *Mechanizacja i Automatyzacja Górnictwa,* 1983, **6** (in Polish).

[36] Sobliatti, G. L.: Propagation equation for a two wire line. *CCITT,* Study Group V—Contribution June 1979, **43**.

[37] Sychev, T. I., Tsapenko, E. F.: Flexible mining cables and network security. Moskva, Izd. Nedra, 1978 (in Russian).

[38] Shchutskii, V. I., Lyakhomskii, A. V.: Statisical characteristics of the parameters of the communication networks of underground electric locomotive transport. Izv. VUZ, *Gornyi Zhurnal,* 1977, **2** (in Russian).

[39] Szulkin, P., Pogorzelski, S.: *Fundamentals of electromagnetic field theory.* Warszawa, WNT, 1964 (in Polish).

[40] Szydło, R.: *Radiocommunication devices in mines.* Katowice, "Śląsk", 1978 (in Polish).

[41] Trubetskov, L. V., Tsygankov, V. E.: *Experimental determination of the law of amplitude distribution of pulse interference in a mine trolley network.* Izv. VUZ, *Gornyi Zhurnal,* 1973, **7** (in Russian).

[42] Vabre, J. P. *Electronique des impulsions,* vol. VI. Masson et Cie, 1972, Paris.

[43] Vaculikova. P., Svoboda, J., Vondrak, M.: RFI Prevention in industrial networks supplying static power converters. *Seventh International Wrocław Symposium on Electromagnetic Compatibility,* Wrocław, 1984.

[44] Vaculikova, P., Svoboda, J., Vondrak, M., Simaček, V.: EMC problems in automated industrial installations with static power converters. *Sixth International Wrocław Symposium on Electromagnetic Compatibility,* Wrocław, 1982.

[45] Valentino, A. R., McLellan, D. W.: ELF Earth return current coupling. *IEEE Transactions on Electromagnetic Compatibility,* November, 1973, Vol. EMC-15, No. 4.

[46] Vance, E. F.: *Coupling to Shielded Cables.* J. Wiley and Sons, New York, London, Sydney, Toronto.

[47] White Donald, R. J.: *A Handbook Series on Electromagnetic Interference and Compatibility.* Don White Consultants Inc., Germantown, Maryland, 1971, 1973.

[48] Wojaczek, A.: Mining telephone sets. *Proceedings of the XIIth Symposium of the Cybernetics in Mining Section,* Committee of Mining, Polish Academy of Sciences, "Theory and Technology of Information Transmission in Mining", Żelazno, 1983 (in Polish).

[49] Wojaczek, A: Trap circuits in mine trolleyphone communication. *Mechanizacja i Automatyzacja Górnictwa,* 1983, **3** (in Polish).

[50] Wojaczek, A.: Elements of adapting an underground traction network to the needs of trolleyphone communication. *Proceedings of the XIIth Symposium of the Cybernetics*

in Mining Section, Committee of Mining, Polish Academy of Science, "Theory and Technology of Information Transmission in Mining", Żelazno, 1983 (in Polish).

[51] Wojaczek, A.: Attempts at radio communication using a loop antenna in headings with electric wire and wireless traction. *Proceedings of the Xth Symposium of the Cybernetics in Mining Section*, Committee of Mining, Polish Academy of Sciences, "Automatization of transport in underground coal and core mining", Jaszowiec 1981 (in Polish).

Standards, regulations, instructions (all in Polish, except 78, 79)

[52] PN-87/E-04650: Environmental Protection of Electrical Products. Names and Specifications.

[53] PN-69/E-02031: Industrial Radioelectric Interference. Permissible Levels.

[54] PN-67/E-04065: Industrial Radioelectric Interference. Laboratory Investigations of Interference Caused by Corona Discharge on Electric High Voltage Devices.

[55] PN-73/E-05108: Industrial Radioelectric Interference. Electric and Motor-Electric Tractions. Permissible Interference Levels. General Requirements and Investigations.

[56] PN-77/E-05118: Industrial Radioelectric Interference. High-Voltage Electric Power Lines and Stations. Permissible Interference Levels. General Requirements and Field Investigations.

[57] PN-79/E-06008: Industrial Radioelectric Interference. General-Use Equipment with Electric Motors. Permissible Interference Levels. General Requirements and Investigations.

[58] PN-70/E-06018: Industrial Radioelectric Interference. Electric Rotating Machines and Industrial Equipment Containing These Machines. Specifications and Investigations.

[59] PN-70/E-06062: Industrial Radioelectric Interference. Anti-interference Chokes. General Requirements and Investigations.

[60] PN-71/E-06208: Industrial Radioelectric Interference. High-Voltage Equipment for Industrial, Medical and Research Purposes. Permissible Interference Levels. General Specifications and Investigations.

[61] PN-79/E-06218: Industrial Radioelectric Interference. Switching and Other Equipment with Movable Contacts. Permissible Interference Levels. General Specifications and Investigations.

[62] PN-76/E-06231: Industrial Radioelectric Interference. Electric Light Fittings for Fluorescent Lamps. Permissible Interference Levels. General Specifications and Investigations.

[63] PN-75/E-08003: Electric Equipment. Anti-shock Protection in Using Interference Eliminators. General Specifications and Investigations.

[64] PN-75/G-39801: Mining Telecommunication Equipment. Fundamental Specifications and Investigations.

[65] PN-70/S-76005: Industrial Radioelectric Interference. Motor-vehicles with Electric Ignition Systems and Equipment with These Engines. Permissible Levels. General Specifications and Investigations.

[66] PN-80/T-01005: Industrial Radioelectric Interference. Fundamental Standards and Specifications.

[67] PN-78/T-04502: Industrial Radioelectric Interference. Typical Methods of Measurement.

[68] PN-68/T-04545: Industrial Radioelectric Interference. Anti-interference Sub-assemblies and Interference Eliminators. Methods of Measurement and Determination of High Frequency Characteristics.

[69] PN-85/T-05208: Industrial Radioelectric Interference. Radio and Television Receivers. Permissible Interference Levels. General Specifications and Investigations.

[70] PN-77/T-06450: Industrial Radioelectric Interference. Equipment for Measurement of Interference. General Specifications and Investigations.

[71] PN-83/T-80002: Interference Suppressor Capacitors. General Specifications and Investigations.

[72] PN-66/T-90310: Local Telephone Cables with Paper Insulation and Metallic Covering. General Specifications and Investigations.

[73] PN-80/T-90320: Low-frequency Telecommunication Stations and Terminating Cables with PVC Insulation and Covering. General Specifications and Investigations.

[74] PN-68/T-90350: Long-Distance Symmetrical Telecommunication Cables with Metallic Covering. General Specifications and Investigations.

[75] BN-76/8984-17: Local Telecommunication Cable Networks. General Specifications and Investigations.

[76] BN-78/8984-18: Long-Distance Telecommunication Cable Lines. General Specifications and Investigations.

[77] BN-75/8984-19: Telecommunication Cable Networks in Plants. Cable Lines. General Specifications and Investigations.

[78] *CCITT*: Directives concernant la protection de lignes de telecommunication contre les actions nuisible des lignes electriques, 1963. Union Internationale des Telecommunications.

[79] *CCITT*: Recommendation Q-23. Orange Book, vol. VI.

[80] Detailed Regulations Concerning Traffic and Bed Economy in Underground Hard and Brown Coal Mining Plants. Ministry of Mining and Power, Katowice, 1984.

[81] Instructions Concerning the Protection of Telecommunication Lines against Harmful Interaction of Electric Power Lines. Vols. A, B, C. Ministry of Communications, Warszawa, 1967.

[82] Instructions Concerning the Protection of Communication Lines and Equipment Against Harmful Interaction of Electric Power Lines and Direct Current Electric Traction. Warszawa, 1974. Annex to the Regulation of the Minister of Communications, Mining and Power, and Transport of the 23rd day of January, 1974.

[83] Technological Instructions concerning Design and Protection of Telecommunication Cables Connected to Electric Power Stations with High Earth Currents. Publication of the Power Studies and Designs Bureau "Energoprojekt" in Poznań, Poznań, 1974.

Subject Index

List of Symbols

$\mathbf{A}$ — vector potential of the electromagnetic field
A — attenuation; wave attenuation
A_{ef} — effective attenuation
A_{fe} — far-end attenuation
A_{ne} — near-end attenuation
$a = -0.5 + j0.5\sqrt{3}$
a_c — asymmetry of the input impedance (capacitive)
$\mathbf{B}$ — magnetic induction
B_i — pulse bandwidth
B_s — noise bandwidth
C — capacity
C_{12} — partial capacity between wire 1 and 2
C_{13} — partial capacity between wire 1 and 3
C_{23} — partial capacity between wire 2 and 3
C_{10} — partial capacity between wire 1 and the earth
C_{20} — partial capacity between wire 2 and the earth
C_{30} — partial capacity between wire 3 and the earth
$\mathbf{D}$ — electric induction
D — diameter of the cable
d — distance between the circuits (conductor, cores, earth)
e — electromotive force of self-induction
E, e — electromotive force
E — rms electromotive force
E_p — electromotive force in pilot core
E_i — electromotive force resulted by mutual inductance
E_i' — induced electromotive force per unit length
E_c — electromotive force resulted by conductance coupling
E_{it} — electromotive force resulted by electric traction line (trolley wire and rails)
E_{ih} — resultant electromotive force excited by electric traction line in heading
$\mathbf{F}$ — force
$F(j\omega)$ — spectrum density
f — frequency

f_i — intermediate frequency

f_h — frequency of heterodyne

f_m — image frequency

G — leakage, conductance of insulation per unit length

g — modulation gain

g' — relative modulation gain

g_m — gradient of transistor characteristic

g_m', g_m'' — derivative of transistor's characteristic

$\mathbf{H}$ — magnetic field intensity

h — pitch of the twist of cores in the cable; distance of wire from foot-wall

I, i — current

I — rms current

I_m — current amplitude

I_1 — current in the disturbing circuit 1 (conductor, line, core)

I_1, I_2, I_3 — current in power cores

I_i — current in earth return line

I_r — current in symmetrical line

$\mathbf{J}$ — electric current density

$j = \sqrt{-1}$

$\mathbf{K}$ — electric field intensity

K_i — induced component of the magnetic field

K_s — static component of the electromagnetic field

K_{ys} — static component of the electromagnetic field parallel to y axis

$k = \sqrt{j\omega\gamma\mu}$

L — inductance

L_p — acoustic pressure level

L_1, L_2, L_3 — power cores number

l — length of the cables, conductors, cores, rails

M — mutual inductance

M_{ab}, M_{ip}, M_{12} — mutual inductance of the two circuits (conductors); mutual inductance between disturbing and disturbed circuits

m — modulation depth; mass

m_{cr} — depth of cross modulation

m_f — modulation index

m_{int} — modulation depth of interference

m_s — modulation depth of a signal

n — characteristic (voltage, current) harmonic number

O_i — receiver immunity to pulse interference

P — power

P_{inn} — power of noise at the input of receiver

P_{ins} — power of signal at the input of receiver

P_{outn} — power of noise at the output of receiver

P_{outs} — power of signal at the output of receiver

p — depth of electromagnetic wave penetration; pulse number of converters

p_f — psophometric weight coefficient at frequency f

q — electric charge

R — radius of the heading; distance

R — resistance, longitudinal resistance

r — radius of conductor

R_i — insulation resistance

r_l — longitudinal resistance of the rails per unit length

r_k — screening factor of the cable armouring

r_m — reduction coefficient of metallic elements

r_r — rail reduction coefficient

r_t — leakage resistance of the rails per unit length

$S(\omega)$ — noise spectral power density

$(S/N)_i$ — signal to noise ratio at the input of receiver

$(S/N)_0$ — signal to noise ratio at the output of receiver

t — time

t_c — charge time constant

t_d — discharge time constant

U, u — voltage

U — rms voltage

U_c — capacitive voltage

U_f — rms voltage harmonic of frequency f

U_{int} — maximum value of interference

U_s — maximum value of a signal

U_r — voltage in a symmetrical line

U_i — voltage in earth return line

U_p — peak value of interference; psophometric voltage of interference

U_l — interference voltage in the contact line

V — scalar potential of an electromagnetic field

v — velocity

W — energy

X — reactance

$X(t)$ — signal

Y — transversal admittance of a line per unit length

Y_{ir} — transverse admittance of the rails per unit length

Y_r — self-admittance of the rail-ground circuit

Z — impedance; longitudinal impedance of a line per unit length

Z_a, Z_b — terminating impedance of a line

Z_{ch} — characteristic impedance

Z_{ex} — external impedance of a wire

Z_i — wave impedance of insulation medium; internal impedance of a source of stray current

Z_{in} — internal impedance of a wire

Z_{ir} — internal impedance of the rails per unit length

Z_r — self-impedance of the rails

Z_s — wave impedance of conductive medium

Z_w — wave impedance

Z_{wr} — wave impedance of a rails to earth circuit

Z_{12} — mutual impedance of two earth return circuit 1 and 2 (per unit length)

α — wave attenuation constant; leakage coefficient of the rails; angle
α_i — attenuation coefficient of wave in insulation medium
α_s — attenuation cofficient of wave in conductive medium
β — phase constant
Γ — propagation coefficient of a line
Γ_r — propagation coefficient of a rails–earth circuit
γ — conductivity
γ_{er} — conductivity of the earth
γ_r — conductivity of the rails
Δf — frequency band
ΔU — voltage drop
ΔY — asymmetry of transverse admittance per unit length
ΔZ — asymmetry of longitudinal impedance per unit length
ε_0 — electric permeability of vacuum
ε_c — complex electric permeability
ε_r — relative permeability of the medium
ε_0 — electric permeability of the vacuum
Φ — magnetic flux
φ — angle
$\varkappa$ — ratio of value of modulation signal to maximum value of modulating signal
λ_e — factor of line susceptibility to electric interaction
λ_i — wave length in insulation medium; coefficient of a line susceptibility to magnetic interaction
λ_s — wave length in a conductive medium
μ — absolute magnetic permeability of a medium
μ_r — relative permeability of a medium
μ_0 — magnetic permeability of a vacuum
ϱ — electric charge density
ψ — angle
Ω_{int} — interference carrier pulsation
Ω_s — signal carrier pulsation
ω — angular frequency
ω_{int} — pulsation modulation of interference
ω_s — pulsation modulating the signal